The Real Happy Valley

The Real Happy Valley

*True stories of crime and heroism from
Yorkshire's front line policewomen*

Alice Vinten

PENGUIN BOOKS

TRANSWORLD PUBLISHERS
Penguin Random House, One Embassy Gardens,
8 Viaduct Gardens, London SW11 7BW
www.penguin.co.uk

Transworld is part of the Penguin Random House group of companies
whose addresses can be found at global.penguinrandomhouse.com

First published in Great Britain in 2023 by Penguin Books
an imprint of Transworld Publishers

A CIP catalogue record for this book is available from the British Library.

ISBN 9781804993460

Typeset in 10.04/15.68pt Optima LT Pro by Jouve (UK), Milton Keynes
Printed and bound in Great Britain by Clays Ltd, Elcograf S.p.A.

The authorized representative in the EEA is Penguin Random House Ireland,
Morrison Chambers, 32 Nassau Street, Dublin D02 YH68.

Penguin Random House is committed to a sustainable future
for our business, our readers and our planet. This book is made
from Forest Stewardship Council® certified paper.

I dedicate this book to the eleven policewomen
who have lost their lives in the line of
duty in the UK since 2000.

Alison Armitage
Catherine Sutcliffe
Sharon Beshenivsky
Siobhan McCann
Cheryl Lloyd
Laura Williams
Fiona Bone
Nicola Hughes
Adele Cashman
Kirsty Nelis
Philippa Reynolds

Introduction

There are many reasons that officers sign up to join the police service. To help their communities, to support people in their time of need, to bring dangerous criminals to justice, to be part of the solution. But right at the core of those reasons, one remains – one desire that is much more powerful than the rest: police officers want to save lives.

When I joined the Metropolitan Police Service in 2004 at age twenty-four, I wanted to help people. I had a strong set of morals and had always been a bit bossy, so I figured policing would suit me nicely. I spent just under eleven years serving on the streets of London. The job was all-encompassing – brilliant and horrifying at the same time – and for the majority of my career in the Met, I absolutely loved it. After the birth of my sons, I became more sensitive to incidents involving children, and I made the decision to leave the service in 2015, mainly for mental health reasons. I remain in awe of the policewomen out there who spend twenty, thirty years, or more, doing such a difficult job.

I've long wanted to write about the incredible things that women can achieve in policing. When I joined the police, I wanted to prove that I could succeed in a 'man's world'. Now that I've left, I want to share the stories of those women who were brave and dedicated enough to spend their whole careers at the sharp end of crime-fighting.

In recent years, UK policing culture has come under the harshest criticism, and most stringent of internal investigations, that it has faced since its inception. Whilst genuine problems around misogyny in policing have been identified, there are many female officers who will still testify that policing is a great career, and things continue to change for the better. Policing is currently facing its biggest challenge yet – restoring the trust of British women. I hope that by sharing the real-life stories of these Yorkshire-based policewomen, and their inspirational careers, I will not only open the public's eyes to the realities of policing as a woman, but also encourage more women to consider a career in the police. According to a report published by GOV.UK in October 2022, just under 35 per cent of UK police officers were women. I'd like to see that figure increase to at least 50 per cent.

I'm passionate about highlighting the amazing things that policewomen can achieve, and I'm also a huge *Happy Valley* fan. Like the rest of the nation, I sat glued to my screen during series one, my mind reeling at the sheer brilliance of its creator Sally Wainwright's ability to present the shocking realities of a woman's life on the front line. An idea started to form in my mind: what if I could combine my love of the programme *and* my passion for championing female police officers?

Sergeant Catherine Cawood, the fictional police officer at the centre of that TV drama, is a no-nonsense, tough-cookie police officer with a complicated personal life. Sally Wainwright's creation of such a 'real' character has been lauded across the TV world and by the public. I think it's easy to forget that police officers are 'real' too – real people with real families, loved ones, and all the intricate problems real life brings. Although Catherine's character is undoubtedly heroic, she's not always the perfect police officer. After the series ended, there were calls on social media for more police officers 'just like Catherine Cawood', and whilst I agree that many of her fictional qualities are perfect for real-life policing – her bravery, instincts, dogged determination and ability to 'cut the shit' – there are also some aspects of Catherine's character that I wouldn't want to see in real life. Having said that, if I was in trouble and had to call 999, and a real-life Sergeant Catherine Cawood arrived, I'd be entirely delighted. And I know who I'd want on my side in a fight.

Many of the scenes in *Happy Valley* involve Catherine talking to her sister, Clare. They ruminate together on the challenges Catherine faces, and show the viewer just how much women can achieve when they support each other. I wanted to have these kinds of conversations with real policewomen. I wanted to interview them, in depth, about the incidents they have dealt with – the things they are proud of – and the people they've saved.

Each chapter in this book describes an incident, or crime, that really happened. Each story was shared with me by real-life Yorkshire policewomen. The women I spoke to are brave, unstoppable, honourable, and were one hundred per cent dedicated to improving the communities they policed. Most of them are retired. It's important to me to prove that middle-aged women are worth listening to.

I have changed the names of all the people involved in these stories, and the contributing officers will remain anonymous. All locations, street names, etc., are false, and every officer in this book works for the fictional 'Yorkshire Police Service'. I have done this to protect the victims of these crimes, their families, and in some cases, the officers themselves. And whilst the names and locations are false, the cases themselves are real, as are the thoughts and feelings of the policewomen who are telling the stories. Every chapter is told in the words of a real-life policewoman, and every incident happened in the area of Yorkshire.

The exception to this rule is chapter four, in which I

share the story of Sharon Beshenivsky, the mother of five and serving police officer who was fatally shot in the line of duty in 2005. Unlike every other chapter of this book, which relies on in-depth interviews with the officers themselves, I have written this chapter based on the news reports of the incident at the time, and since, including the real names of those convicted of the crime. This chapter should, therefore, be seen as a dramatization of Sharon's tragic murder, as I did not feel that I could write about the policewomen of Yorkshire without telling the story of the ultimate sacrifice Sharon was forced to make as she tried to protect the public on her beat.

Though the true stories in this book have happened in Yorkshire, they are representative of the amazing and dedicated work that policewomen across the country achieve on a daily basis. The stories in this book could happen, and have happened, and keep on happening, all across the UK.

Chapter 1

Nearly every police officer, by the time they reach the end of their career, will have talked at least one person out of suicide. Whilst the vast majority of the public would see this as saving a person's life, most officers would consider it just another part of the day job. Like me, many hardcore *Happy Valley* fans got sucked right in from episode one, where we see fictional Sergeant Catherine Cawood talking down a suicidal youth who has doused himself in petrol. In her usual upfront, no-nonsense style, Catherine manages to break down the barrier of her uniform by personalizing herself in just three brilliant sentences in which she explains her personal situation – divorced, middle-aged, living with her recovering drug addict sister, having two adult children although one is dead, the other estranged – by way of showing the boy that things aren't so rosy in her life either and engaging him in conversation to stop his suicide attempt.

Every copper has their own life experiences and each one will bring those experiences to an incident in a different way. Just as the fictional Sergeant Catherine Cawood suffers flashbacks of her daughter's suicide throughout *Happy Valley*, which threatens to destroy her mental health, it doesn't stop her from doing her job. The same is true in real life.

Police officers have to turn up. They can't just walk away when their shift is over, or if they're tired, fed up or emotional. The buck stops with them. Despite having set hours, not everyone gets to go home on time, as Sergeant Kate Dungay experienced many times throughout her career.

Police Sergeant Kate Dungay pushes wearily into the exit door, using the weight of her tired body to swing it outwards, a blast of cold air making her shiver as she steps from the police station into the yard. She's just finished a ten-hour night shift and can't wait to get home to her bed. The fresh October morning air does nothing to stave off her aching exhaustion. Yawning, she rummages in her trouser pocket for her car keys, ambling towards where she thinks she parked. She can hear some kind of commotion coming from the back of the car park, but her ears are closed to it. *Let someone else sort that out*, she thinks. *I've dealt with enough for one shift.* Being the duty sergeant, she'd been responsible for her team for the Friday night shift. It had started with pub fights, where no one wanted to press charges – her team holding head wounds together and shoving non-cooperative people into ambulances. Then came the domestics, seven across their patch, just as the pubs began to empty out and drunk husbands came home to their wives. Two men arrested for assault. One female for drink-driving. That carried them through to the early morning, when anyone not already tucked away with a prisoner was out cruising the streets, putting their hands in pockets.

She'd had a lot of paperwork to complete and supervise by the end of the shift and she rubs her eyes as she makes it to her car. Plugging the key into the driver's door, her shoulders hunch as she hears footsteps quickly approach her from behind.

'Sarge,' a voice says.

Kate lets out a deep sigh, lowering her shoulders and turning round. The PC in front of her is red in the face, panting lightly. 'Glad I caught you,' he puffs, his breath making him look like he's doing a childish impression of a steam train. 'There's a man threatening to throw himself off the roof of the old library.' He points to the end of the car park, and Kate realizes that this must have been the commotion she heard as she left the station.

'And that's my problem how?' she asks, thinking that if

he'd been a minute slower, she'd have been driving out the gate.

'Yeah – sorry – it's just, our sergeant doesn't start till eight.'

'Fuck's sake,' she mutters under her breath. All she wants to do is leave. She can feel the cold metal of her car keys digging into her palm as she clenches her fists. She looks at her watch – five past six. *Fuck.*

Kate has taken off her jacket to reveal her jumper, epaulettes displaying her sergeant's stripes. She's sent the apologetic PC back into the station to fetch her a radio, and she's standing at the back of the car park, looking up at the man on the roof. Her brain tells her that if he really wanted to jump, he'd have done it by now, but she shakes the thought away. She's the sergeant on scene. The buck stops with her.

'Morning, fella.' He turns to look at her, wobbling precariously towards the edge as he does so. She puts her hands out in front of her, palms facing towards him. 'Whoa – easy – no dancing, please.'

He's a big guy. Looks about forty years old. Bulky and heavy-set, he must be well over six feet tall but it's hard to tell from this angle. He's wearing a dark hoody, which hangs open to reveal a crumpled chequered shirt beneath. It has wet patches across the front. Kate wonders if it's beer. He's got week-old stubble and his hair looks as though it's been left to grow out.

'Don't come any closer!' he shouts, and she almost rolls her eyes at the well-worn phrase. 'I'll fucking jump.' Her eyes are drawn to his hands as he waves them about, like two bunches of thick butcher's sausages, fingers red and angry in the cold.

She considers the drop. The library was built around 1990, an imposing building that stands at least thirty feet high. The central roof area is taller, with a flat roof surrounding it, and narrow ledges surrounding that. It's built in red brick, with white concrete details. The man has climbed over the low parapet that borders the roof, and is standing on a ledge that looks around two feet wide. He could easily die from that fall, Kate thinks, especially if he goes headfirst. Looking up at him, she notices he's still swaying. She wonders if he's been drinking. And although she's known for having a nose like a bloodhound, she can't smell him from this distance.

'Okay,' she placates him, taking a step back, 'I'm staying here.' She's around five metres from the base of the building, and running around its boundary are cast-iron railings, with pointed tips. She imagines him landing on those spikes and decides it's definitely an outcome that she needs to prevent.

'I'll fucking do it!' he shouts. 'I've got nothing to live for – I'm fucking done.'

He teeters, toes of his scuffed trainers poking precariously over the edge of the narrow ledge.

Kate's stomach dips, as if she's just driven over a sharp hill. All thoughts of getting home to her bed disappear as she focuses on the man. She doesn't know what he's done. She doesn't know why he's up there. But she knows she does not want him to fall.

Where the hell is that radio? She turns briefly back towards the nick, sees the puffed-out PC quick-stepping his way across the car park and jerks her thumb at him – *hurry up!* – causing him to break into a trot. Turning back to the man on the roof, she shouts again, 'Let's just talk about it, okay? I'm not going to do anything except talk to you. What's your name?'

'Fuck off!' He waves his arms wildly, as if trying to swat her away, once again swaying dangerously close to the edge. 'You're not going to change my mind!'

Finally, the radio is placed into her hand, and Kate brings it to her lips, keeping her voice low. 'Control, from Sergeant Dungay.'

'*G'ahead, Kate.*'

'I'm going to need ambulance and fire standing by in Colby Street, but I want them on silent approach, please. No lights or sirens or we'll spook this bloke off the roof.'

'*Understood.*'

'Also, please tee up the force negotiators,' Kate says, hopeful that they may by some miracle be nearby and come and take over from her.

'*Received, trying them now.*'

Kate knows that the man will need immediate medical assistance if he falls. Having an ambulance round the corner could save precious seconds. And if he agrees to come down, the fire service may be of use. Either that or they'll be able to cut through the railings if he ends up impaled. A series of sounds and images runs through Kate's head – dead bodies in various stages of decay, the face of a crying loved one, the scream of a woman falling – like a horror-movie reel.

A crowd has started to gather and she can hear people murmuring behind her. To her disgust, somebody shouts 'Jump!' and the man on the roof begins to cry, hacking out large, ugly gulps. She turns to the PC, rooted in place beside her, and growls at him, 'Get those fucking people back,' before raising her radio once more. 'Control, I'm going to need at least one more PC or PCSO out here for crowd control, and somebody get me a bloody chair.'

'Received, Sergeant.'

'Find out if anyone knows who he is.' This to the PC, who nods, moving towards the crowd.

She turns back to the man and decides to be honest. 'Listen, ignore them, they're a bunch of rubbernecking idiots.' She continues, 'My name's Kate and I've just come off a ten-hour night shift so I'm bloody knackered. But that's fine, I'm used to being knackered, I'm a single mum with three kids and shifts to manage.'

The man regards her from the roof, and she takes the fact that he's no longer telling her to fuck off as a sign to continue. 'Nothing's ever as bad as you think, most things can be sorted out with a bit of a chat, so why don't you tell me what's going on?'

He looks behind her and Kate turns to see the station officer, Rose, carrying a plastic chair towards her. Rose sets it next to Kate with a wink and retreats to the relative safety of the station.

'Look, I'm going to sit down as, like I said, I'm bloody

knackered.' She lowers herself into the chair with a groan. 'Why don't you sit down too? It would make me feel a lot better if you weren't wobbling around all over the place on that ledge.'

The man suddenly lurches forward and Kate jumps out of her chair, but he bends his knees and lowers himself onto his bottom. His legs dangle over the ledge and Kate is reminded of a toddler sitting on a seat that's too big for him. She relaxes slightly now that he's sitting down, and lowers herself back into her chair.

'How'd you get up there, anyway?'

'Drainpipe.' He points his thumb behind him, in the direction of the street, and Kate realizes that he must have climbed up the front of the building, scaled the triangular roof in the centre and ended up on this side. She wonders why he's chosen to try to top himself right next to the police station and then immediately answers her own question – because he wants somebody to stop him.

Kate's radio pipes up and she raises it to her ear, keeping the volume low.

'Right, there's good news and bad news. The bad news is the negotiators are at least an hour away. The good news is someone in the crowd has given us a name. Kevin Glendale. We're doing some digging now.'

'All received,' Kate confirms wearily. She's stuck here. Her eyes run along multiple cracks in the masonry, assessing the stability of the building. The library itself closed some time ago, and the building is on its way to ruin. She examines the ledge Kevin is sitting on, imagining it crumbling beneath him. They're nowhere near out of the woods yet. At least they've got a name. She knows that the officers in the control room will be checking the PNC, the Police National Computer, for his name as she sits here worrying about erosion. Hopefully they will get some details that might help her talk him down.

'So, what's happened to lead you up there this morning, then?' she attempts. Now that the crowd has moved back, she no longer needs to shout, just raising her voice a little. Everyone's always said she's got a loud voice – a voice for policing – and she's grateful for it now.

'Me girlfriend's kicked me out and she won't let me see my baby.' He shouts it through gritted teeth, veins sticking out on his neck. 'I was doing really well. I'd even stopped thieving, like. Then the stupid bitch kicks me out. Decides she's too good for me – changes the locks! Even calls the police on me.'

A tingle at the back of Kate's neck: *why has his girlfriend had to call us?* She's not about to ask him, she wants to keep him onside, not hold him to account. Before she can ask any follow-up questions, he continues.

'My boy was the only thing I had to live for.' He starts sobbing again, wiping his nose roughly with the sleeve of his hooded top. 'I've got nothing now, coz of that selfish cow. Who the fuck does she think she is? Keeping me away from my baby? I thought everything was going fine, and now this.' He pauses, before shouting 'Fuck this!' at the top of his lungs.

The crowd in the distance cheers and Kate rolls her eyes.

She thinks about addressing him by name, but decides to wait until he gives it to her to use it. She doesn't want to do anything that will set him off. Now that she's involved, she's responsible for him. If he jumps, it's her that'll have to justify what she did to try to stop him.

'She'll calm down in a bit, eh? Let you see littl'un?'

''S too late,' he shouts, 'we've been to court. They've banned me.' He's starting to work himself up again, rocking backwards and forwards on the ledge.

Looking up at him is giving her neck ache, and she holds the back of her neck as she tries to keep him calm, ignoring the discomfort. 'How many times have you been to court?'

'Once.'

'Okay, then.' She tries to keep her voice light and enthusiastic. 'It's probably just an interim order, just a temporary thing. Maybe just for a few weeks until things calm down.'

'No, you don't get it, fuck's sake!' Still shouting, he starts slapping himself in the face. The sounds of the slaps echo across the car park and set Kate's teeth on edge. He jumps to his feet, torso once again leaning way out over the ledge as he does it. She imagines a boxer, before a match, slapping himself in the face to psych himself up. Ready to fight. Ready to *jump*.

'That bitch has told them all kinds of lies, she's turned them against me.' He's spitting out the words. 'I'd *never* hurt my son – she's the one that wants to go out with her mates, probably fucking everything that moves. I wouldn't have to get angry in the first place if she wasn't such a whore. I'd *never* hurt him – never!'

Kate looks at him up there, panting, red in the face, tendons bulging in his neck. He's totally unable – or unwilling – to control his temper. Maybe she can believe that he wouldn't deliberately hurt his child, but angry people are reckless. She imagines a baby being in the vicinity of his rage right now, imagines a terrified mother holding a baby to her chest as his spittle hits her in the face and his voice hurts tiny eardrums. She firmly believes that if a man is abusing his partner, mentally or physically, then he is also abusing his children. Children can't live in a home with this kind of screaming and not be hurt by it.

As she looks up at his true character, at the roiling, buzzing rage of him, she feels like letting him jump. She's had a long shift. She's had a long career, in fact, of dealing with men like him. Of listening to them twist the truth and blame everybody but themselves for their own destructive behaviour. He continues to shift precariously close to the edge, his temper blinding him to the danger of the spikes below.

She's got to calm him down. 'I do get it!' she shouts. 'I nearly lost my kids.'

That gets his attention. His hands drop to his sides and he tilts his head towards her.

'I've been through family court. Through it forwards and backwards, mate. My ex tried to take my kids away too.' He's the last person she wants to discuss her personal life with but, frankly, she's desperate to get him off the roof safely and it just comes out. 'Our divorce got bitter and he used the kids to punish me.'

'Sergeant Dungay, receiving Control?'

She holds a finger up to Kevin. 'Hold that thought.'

Making sure the radio is still turned down, she holds it to her ear. 'Go ahead.'

'Are you safe to talk?'

This is police code for *is the suspect within earshot?* Control obviously has some intelligence to pass to her that they don't want the suspect to overhear. 'Yes, he's still on the roof.'

'So – no surprises – he's known to police. He's got previous for shoplifting, possession of cannabis, but most of his offences are domestic assaults. He's also got warnings for violence, assault on police and mental health. Intelligence shows that he's attempted suicide before whilst in police custody. We've got his last known address, d'you want me to send a unit over there?'

'No, hold off,' Kate replies. 'He's been kicked out. Last thing we want is the ex-girlfriend turning up and spurring him on.'

'Got ya, skip. Also, we got ambo and fire standing by. They're monitoring this channel so shout if you need them.'

''Cieved, thanks.'

She makes a quiet request of the control room, which they agree to fulfil, before she lowers her radio again.

'Sorry about that,' Kate calls upwards, and Kevin nods. He's finally still, staring out over the rooftops. Kate takes a moment to process the information she's been given. *Previously attempted suicide.* There's two ways you could look at that, she thinks. If he's attempted to kill himself before but never managed it then he probably wasn't really trying. On the other hand, many people kill themselves without meaning to. It does nothing to lower her risk assessment. He could still jump. *Domestic assaults.* This new information may explain the real reason that a judge decided he couldn't have access to his son. If he's a domestic abuser then he, quite rightly, may never get contact back.

Kate considers the man above her from a different angle. No longer a desperate father devastated at losing a son, but a dangerous domestic abuse perpetrator too violent to be trusted with children. She looks at his strong frame and thick arms. Imagines him shouting like he was just minutes ago, but this time it's in his partner's face. She's crying, and he's just getting closer and closer, until she's shoved against a wall. Kate feels heat in her chest as her heart starts to beat quicker. Her cheeks flame. Anger. Shame. She shakes her head. No matter what he's done, she is a police officer. She needs to get him safely off this roof.

'Kevin, is it?' She decides to take the risk. She doesn't know if it's because she cares about him less now, or because she's hoping a personal touch will get him down quicker.

'Yeah – Kev.' He raises an eyebrow at her. 'Bet you know all about me now, don't you?'

'Only your name.' She smiles, urging herself to make it look genuine. 'Listen, we can't talk about this properly while you're up there, and it's bloody freezing. Why don't you come down?'

He starts shaking his head, his body swaying with the motion. 'I know you plods, you'll nick me the moment my foot touches the ground.'

'Like I said, I can help you – I've been there,' Kate coaxes. 'I can talk you through the family-court system, I can even put you in touch with experts who can help you through it.' She rubs her hands together, the ends of her fingers starting to go numb in the cold.

He's still shaking his head, then leans forward, bunching his fists into his hair. He starts rocking again and with every forward swing Kate imagines him pitching headfirst onto the railings below. His words come out in ragged sobs. 'I've fucked it all up. I've fucked it! I can't come down coz you'll nick me and then I'll definitely never see him again, will I? They'll say I'm a nutter. Nutters can't have children. No, no, fuck it all, I should just do it and get it over with.' His last words come out in a tortured growl. He leans forward, looking straight down. His face is pale and sweaty, his hair sticking to his forehead even in the frigid October air. He's looking straight at the railings, and Kate decides to try a risky tactic.

'Have you ever seen someone get stuck on railings like those?'

He shakes his head, still looking down.

'I have.' The memory of a colleague who fell from a roof. 'He fell. Three of those massive spikes went straight through his thigh. He was pinned there for two hours, at a horrible angle. I've never heard a man make noises like that. The firemen had to use a huge angle grinder to cut him free. He hasn't walked right since.' She pauses, watching how Kevin is taking this. His hands have tightened into fists. 'If you jump from there, you probably won't even die, you'll just get stuck on those railings. I can't imagine the pain.'

Kevin's face has turned grey, but he stares at Kate and clenches his jaw. 'Maybe I'll aim for them.' His face is twisted. 'Headfirst should do it.'

'I don't think you will.' Kate crosses her arms and meets his gaze. 'You don't look like a quitter to me.'

'How the fuck would you know?'

'Because I'm a parent too.'

His eyes widen. Kate sees that she's finally getting through to him and ploughs on. 'You may not be able to see your son at the moment, but he's still out there. He still needs you. He'll always need you.' She stands up, taking a step towards him, looking up at the vertiginous ledge and trying to swallow back the nausea. 'You know what? I wanted to give up too. But I didn't. I didn't give up – I persevered – because that's what you have to do when you're a parent. That's *all* being a parent is, facing one day after the next. You've got to keep going – for them. For your son.'

Footsteps behind her, and she takes the opportunity to ram her point home.

'If you jump off this roof today, you'll be giving up on your son. Don't do that to him. You still have a chance to make it right.'

Rose appears once again and hands Kate the items she requested earlier. A packet of cigarettes, a coffee and a lighter. She just hopes he's a smoker.

'Come down.' She takes a sip of coffee, warming her cold hands on the cup, before balancing it on the arm of the chair. Then she takes out a cigarette, lights it and takes a long drag, letting herself sigh contentedly, and audibly, as she releases the smoke from her lungs. She rarely smokes, usually only when she's had a drink, but Kevin doesn't need to know that.

'There's one of these in the nick for you' – she points the cigarette at the coffee – 'and I'll give you the rest of this packet if you come down.'

He's looking longingly at the cigarette. *Bingo.*

'Promise you won't arrest me?'

'Kev – you know I can't make promises like that. But I can promise you this. My priority is your safety. I want you off that roof and in the warm, with a nice cuppa and a ciggie, so we can sort out all this mess.'

Kate knows exactly what she's going to do when he gets down, and that's detain him under Section 136 of the Mental Health Act. It gives the police power to detain and remove anyone who is in danger of hurting themselves or others, so long as they're in a public place. By force if necessary.

Kevin sighs and nods quickly. He stands up, and as he's turning around to climb back over the parapet, one of his feet slips, causing him to swing backwards – *Kate sees him fall, a slow-motion reel in another bad movie, a sickening thud as he bounces off the railings and onto the concrete below* – but at the last second, he miraculously catches the edge of the brickwork with his fingers, rights himself and is back onto the relative safety of the flat roof.

'Fucking hell,' Kate exhales, bending over like she's been punched in the stomach, as her vision swims. She wonders for the millionth time if she has PTSD, and whether she should see someone about it, rubbing the back of her neck as she straightens and begins to walk around the building. She wonders if having him climb back down the way he went up is a good idea; maybe she should have asked the fire truck to come round and they could have used their cherry picker. But something told her that Kevin would bask in the attention of new emergency workers, and she didn't want to have to listen to his story all over again.

She updates Control that he's coming down and follows his progress back across the roof. She asks for a couple of officers to join her at the base of the large iron drainpipe on the other side of the building. She can see how he got up there so easily. The pipe is secured with thick metal struts at regular intervals all the way up to the roof. It's almost like a ladder. Kevin appears over her head and two officers from a different team to hers arrive as he begins to carefully clamber down. Kate indicates to one of them to pass her their cuffs. They nod at her, and as Kevin's bottom foot touches the pavement, they grab a shoulder each, pressing him against the wall.

'You pigs!' Kevin screams. 'You fucking promised.'

Kate steps between the two officers and places Kevin in handcuffs. She talks into his ear, keeping her voice low and clear. 'I didn't promise anything, Kevin. The cuffs are just until we get you somewhere safe.'

He continues to shout and swear as the officers begin to walk him back to the police station, one on each arm. Now that she's close enough, Kate can smell the alcohol seeping out of his pores. He must have been drinking for hours before climbing up there, it's a miracle he hadn't fallen.

As they get into the police station, Kevin starts to quieten down. His shouting turns to sobbing and he repeats, 'You lied to me. You promised you wouldn't arrest me.'

'I didn't promise that,' Kate sighs, 'and you've not been arrested. As I said, I want to make sure you're safe. I didn't want you getting any silly ideas and trying to run off, did I? You've been detained under Section 136 of the Mental Health Act, do you understand what that means?'

'Yeah.' Kevin suddenly seems resigned to his fate, and they walk him into a cell – the only secure room they have available to keep him safe until mental health professionals arrive. Kate has been updated via the radio that he has a mental health worker and that she's on her way.

'If I didn't get you in here, safe, then you would've been out there getting yourself into all kinds of trouble. Now, if you stay calm for the next few minutes whilst I make you that cuppa, we can get those cuffs off. One of the detention officers will be able to take you out for a ciggie too.'

Kevin nods, lowering himself onto the bench in the cell like it's somewhere familiar.

Kate leaves the two PCs to keep a constant watch on

Kevin. She walks towards the sergeants' office, sighing and rubbing her eyes. She's got a shitload of paperwork to do.

It's 10 a.m., and the winter sun is clear in the sky, but somehow it feels even colder the second time Kate pushes through the exit door and into the car park. It's blissfully silent in the yard. She heads towards her car, opening the door quickly and jumping inside. She cranks the air to hot, knowing that she's got at least five minutes of freezing air pumping out before the heater will kick in, and turns the flow to low. She'll allow herself a blast of heat at the start of the journey. She won't be able to get too comfortable on the drive home because warmth will lead to her exhausted eyes closing. Despite having two coffees since getting Kevin safely off the roof, she could still fall asleep at any moment. The last part of her thirty-minute drive home will be spent with the driver's window wide open, cold air blasting into her face to keep her awake.

As she pulls out of the back yard, she thinks about Kevin. She'd read his conviction record and the social services reports about his girlfriend and son. He'd not only been convicted of beating her whilst she was pregnant, but he'd also abused numerous previous girlfriends before that. She thinks about how he was blaming the mother of his child up on the roof. Of the names he was calling her. Typical perpetrator behaviour. Blaming everyone but himself. He saw himself as the victim, ignoring the real victims of his abuse. The irony was that his girlfriend hadn't wanted to chuck him out. Social services had told her that if she didn't end the relationship – if she didn't protect her son from Kevin's abuse – they would take the baby into care. She'd chosen her son.

Kate pulls away from the town and onto the winding lanes of the countryside, her eyes scanning the low, far-away hills, the winter sun making her squint. This is her favourite part of the commute, leaning in to the curves of the country roads. She winds down the windows and sucks in the fresh Yorkshire air as she wonders what Kevin's child-hood was like. She doesn't know for sure, but she'd bet good money that he grew up in a house with violence. The eighties were hard for many families in this area and it was a time when women didn't ask for help, when abuse was hidden behind thick brown and orange curtains. Like the ones in her family home.

She starts to worry about what she said to him earlier. She'd encouraged him. She'd told him not to give up, that she was sure he would see his son again. She curses her-self. Has she doomed his ex-partner to a life of court battles? Has she given him the confidence not to back down? Guilt starts to seep into her pores as she runs over their conversa-tion in her head, doubting herself. She doesn't like to admit it, but she has frequent battles with her mind after tense or upsetting incidents. The temptation to pull your words and actions apart is too strong, and she starts to berate herself. Why did you believe him when he said he was a good father? *Idiot.* Have you learnt nothing? *Stupid.* She hears the insults in the voice of her stepfather. Then, her own voice cuts in. You said what you needed to. You got him off the roof. The courts are protecting his child, that's what matters. He's a feckless drunk who'll give up on his son. Which is the best thing for the child.

She pulls into her driveway and turns off the engine. Leaning her head back, she takes a minute to decompress before heading into her house. She doesn't like to bring things home. Despite trying to clear her mind, she does what she does after every domestic incident she deals with. She thinks about the cycle. About how every person who lives in a house with domestic abuse seems to be indelibly marked by it. How daughters grow up and choose abusers, because that's what they've learnt is normal. How sons grow up and choose to abuse. She knows, of course, that this is a generalization, that some people escape the cycle.

She hauls herself out of her car and heads to the front door. She's glad Kevin doesn't have access to his son and she hopes that his girlfriend sticks to her guns and doesn't take him back. The cynical part of her mind says, *they always take them back.*

She shuts the door quietly, hangs up her coat and keys and heads straight upstairs. Before climbing into bed, she pops her head around her son's door. Seventeen, and still in a safe, deep sleep that will probably last way past midday. She smiles and quietly pads to her room.

A rogue thought slips into her mind.

Should've let him jump.

She's too tired to tell it to shut up.

PC Kate Dungay served eighteen years in the Yorkshire Police Service. During that time, she progressed upwards to the rank of Inspector and worked predominantly in the fast-paced world of response policing. She also spent time working in custody, the VIPER Identification Unit and Divisional Intelligence Unit. In her early years of policing, she received a personal letter of thanks from a chief constable after rescuing and successfully resuscitating a woman who was trapped in a house fire.

Kate described her career as *'varied, sometimes challenging, but extremely rewarding.'*

Chapter 2

Police officers work within a tight set of guidelines, laws and policies. Whilst many television detectives earn their fearsome reputations by 'bending the rules', in reality, stepping outside of accepted practice is fraught with danger for warranted officers. One tweak of the rules can mean that a whole court case is thrown out, and a step too close to satisfying a fiery temper can ruin a career.

Sergeant Cawood, as a fictional character, is officially a *badass*. However, like most popular television characters, she does have the occasional moral shortcoming. She roughly grabs the testicles of a young man who makes an inappropriate comment about the death of PC Kirsten McAskill, and illegally forces entry into Ashley Cowgill's flat looking for Tommy Lee Royce. As viewers, we wholeheartedly support Catherine when she breaks these rules; we see her willingness to get things done as a strength, not a weakness. But how would we feel if a real police officer acted the same way?

Is it ever possible for real police officers to *think outside the box*? Is there room for creative thinking, within the rules, and are arrest figures, conviction rates and tangible results the only way to measure good policing? PC Lisa Groome has police boots that are well worn from walking the fine line between professionalism and good old-fashioned getting the job done.

Monday, 10 a.m.

PC Lisa Groome winces as Rose calls her name. She curses herself, for the umpteenth time, for turning her head too quickly.

'There's a young girl at the front desk – she's reet jittery – saying she wants to speak to a female officer.'

Lisa's been off active patrol for a month now, and she frequently wonders if her neck is ever going to get better. It had suddenly locked into place three months ago when she was driving a patrol car. The embarrassment of having to call a colleague to come and rescue her still makes her cheeks redden. After two months of intensive treatment, she was cleared to come back to work, but only on 'light duties'. There was no chance in hell that she could turn and check her blind spot, so driving was out the window. On the streets she'd be a risk to herself and her colleagues. Which led her here. Her team was full of creaking officers, who were either injured or soon to be sent out to pasture. Their role was to take the pressure off the front-line teams by searching through crime reports to see if anything could be dealt with over the phone. That, and they would deal with any members of the public who turned up at the front desk and wanted to speak to a police officer. At first, she'd thought that maybe she'd be glad of the break. Being able to eat her food hot and go to the toilet when she liked hadn't sounded too bad. But she desperately missed the action of the streets. At least she was a little more comfortable, only having to wear her police shirt and trousers. No need to cart around your kit belt and stab vest when you weren't out on the streets.

She grabs her pocket book and pen and heads after Rose, who's already marching back to the front office. She feels tired, her neck is sore and she has a building resentment about the fact that she's essentially been lowered to the role of a glorified receptionist. She walks out into the public waiting area and sees a young Asian woman wringing her hands by the counter. She can't be much more than eighteen and she's wearing baggy, bland clothes and a beige hijab. At her feet are four large carrier bags full of groceries. The look of abject terror on the girl's face knocks the resentment out of Lisa.

'This way.' Lisa points to the interview rooms, waiting for the girl to go ahead of her. 'First door on the left.'

The girl stands by the door uncertainly, and Lisa pushes

it open for her. The girl steps in like a prey animal stepping
out of its den, eyes darting to all four corners of the room.
Lisa points to a chair, realizing that the girl needs directing
to take each step forward, and lowers herself carefully into
a seat across from her. She watches in silence as the woman
carefully places her shopping bags on the floor and perches
on the edge of a chair.

'You're safe here, love.'

The girl looks as if she feels anything but safe.

'What's your name?'

The girl freezes, just an almost imperceptive shake of her
head giving away how uncomfortable she is with that
question.

'Why don't you tell me why you're here?'

'I – we need to be quick.' The girl speaks in a soft voice,
a Yorkshire voice. 'I don't have much time.'

Despite being in a police station, with a female officer,
in a private room with no windows, the girl still looks as
if she's expecting something awful to happen at any
moment.

'Have you got a bus to catch or something?' Lisa asks,
keeping her voice light. She doesn't want to scare the girl
off by adopting too serious a tone; she seems flighty.

'No.' The girl closes her eyes briefly, as if she needs to will
herself to keep talking. 'They time me when I leave the house.'

'What do you mean, they time you?' Lisa leans forward.
She wants to open her pocket book and click on her pen
but stops herself. Like a rabbit in the headlights, any sudden
movements and this girl will run.

'I'm allowed to catch the bus to get the shopping in, but I only have an hour.' She wrings her small hands. 'If I'm not back on the right bus I'll get into trouble.'

'Who is it that's timing you?'

'My mother-in-law, my husband.' She looks at her fingers, twisted round themselves. 'His entire family.'

'Are you safe there?' Lisa asks. 'Do they hurt you physically?'

The woman's lips tighten into a thin line. 'I'm okay if I do what I'm told' – she glances down at her watch – 'but if they find out I'm here . . .' She shifts in her seat and Lisa leans forward, placing a gentle hand on the woman's forearm, convinced that she's about to bolt.

'You don't have to go back there. I – we – can keep you safe. We can find you a place in a refuge, we can make sure they don't find you.' But the girl is shaking her head, shrinking back from Lisa's touch, before she can finish her plea.

'He'll find me.' Her chest heaves up and down. 'He'll find me, I'll bring shame upon my family, their family – the whole community!' She jolts up from her chair and makes for the door.

'Wait – please.' Lisa stands. 'I'm not going to force you to do anything. I can see how difficult it must have been for you to come here – how brave you've been to speak to me.' The woman lifts her chin, meeting Lisa's eye. 'All I ask is that you come back. Come back and talk to me, no pressure. I won't force you to do anything.'

A moment of silence. Lisa is facing the woman, arms outstretched, palms up. *Please.*

A tiny nod. 'Next week, same time.'

Lisa leads the fragile woman out of the interview-room corridor and back into the front office, watches as she scurries out the door, eyes on the ground in front of her. She rushes in the direction of the bus stop, thin arms pulled pencil straight by the weight of her bags, shoulders slumped by the weight of her suffering.

Hands on her hips, Lisa wonders if she should follow her. She dismisses the idea quickly, a tiny shake of her head as she walks back to her office. There's no way she'd be able to get on the same bus without being seen, and she can't risk breaking the woman's trust. If she does, she is certain she'll never see her again. She feels a heat in her chest as she imagines how the woman is being treated at home, a fierce wave of protectiveness washing over her. She'd like to meet this husband of hers.

Back at her desk, she jots down the time and date in her diary, circling it three times. She makes some brief notes in her pocket book.

What if she doesn't come back?

Monday, 10 a.m.

Lisa paces back and forth across the station office.

'You'll wear a hole in t'carpet if you don't pack that in,' Rose observes.

'Shit,' Lisa exhales through her teeth. *She's not coming. She can't get out. Something's happened to her.* All week

Lisa's mind had conjured up different ways that the woman could be exposed, her deceit discovered. What if a family member was following her? What if someone from her community saw her enter the police station? Not for the first time, Lisa imagines attending an emergency call at an ordinary house, in an ordinary street, and finding the woman's body. She's seen the dead bodies of beaten wives far too often not to consider death as a very real outcome for the frightened girl.

She thinks back to the discussion she had with her skipper last week. Sergeant Tony Stamp was a year off retirement and had mentally already packed up his desk and left the building. He had a red, bald head and a huge beer belly. He'd displayed frustration that Lisa had let the woman go.

'We'll be criticized for not safeguarding her.' He'd mimed air quotes when he'd said the word safeguarding, which immediately got Lisa's back up.

Lisa had pointed out that they had no powers to force her to give her details or keep her at the police station, adding, 'I get the sense that we need to play the long game with this one. I'll try and get more details next time.'

Tony had tutted. 'If she wants our help she needs to bloody well cooperate. Honestly, if it's so bad there why has she gone back? She's probably after a move on t'council.'

Lisa had tried not to roll her eyes directly into the sergeant's face and excused herself. Alone in the ladies, Lisa scrunched up her face and mimicked Tony in the mirror. She stuck out her belly and grunted dementedly until she choked out a bitter laugh. Idiot. Men like Tony were all too common in her job – labelling women as attention seekers, of lying to get what they want, of *tricking* or *trapping* innocent men at every opportunity. They should just say what they mean and call us all witches, she thought angrily as she scrubbed her hands. As she dried them, she reminded herself that all she can do is rise above. Keep doing the best she can for women. And let the dinosaurs like Tony age out of the force.

The front office is separated from the public by the counter. On Lisa's side, it looks like every other office in the nick – tired carpet, piles of paper, fluorescent jackets discarded on office chairs. There's a helmet on one of the desks. Lisa grabs it and flips it upside down. On the inside, a worryingly detailed penis has been drawn in thick black marker. She shakes her head, placing the helmet back on the desk. Anything discarded is graffitied.

There are three doors leading from the station office. The first goes out into the public counter area, a high counter at a right angle, clear safety Perspex from the desk to the ceiling, with slots at the bottom that allow paperwork and small items to be passed in and out. The counter faces out onto the entrance doors and the public area, a small rectangle lined with chairs, walls plastered with information leaflets and 'missing' posters, and a phone on the wall that calls through to the custody suite. There's a bell that the public can press for attention.

The second door leads to the inner station, the cells and offices, and the third leads to the interview rooms and a small hallway that connects to the public entrance area via a secure door, where people can be buzzed in if necessary. This is where, a week earlier, Lisa had led the frightened woman into a private room. Lisa hovers by this doorway now, glancing from Rose back to the interview room she has reserved for the woman. She must make sure no one else nabs it before she gets here. *If she gets here.*

The buzzer sounds loudly, making Lisa jump. Rose nods at Lisa and heads to the counter, before returning a second later. 'You're on.'

Lisa rushes to the secure door and jabs in the code before swinging the door open and motioning for the woman to come in. She stands by the counter in the same drab clothes she was wearing last week. A small smile crosses her face as she sees Lisa and hurries towards her. Lisa has made sure that they've got the same room as last time. She wants the woman to feel that she's somewhere familiar – that she's safe. If only for the short time she's with Lisa.

The woman walks straight to the chair that she sat in previously and lowers her bags to the floor with a short puff.

'I'm glad you came back,' Lisa says with a smile.

The woman nods.

'I want to hear more about what you're going through. Do you think maybe you could tell me your name?'

A frown crosses the woman's face, and Lisa holds her breath.

'Asha,' the woman whispers.

'Asha,' Lisa repeats, nodding in acknowledgement of the woman's bravery, 'thank you.'

Asha is quicker to talk today, she knows their time is short and the words tumble from her mouth as if she wants to cram the room with them, squeeze them into the corners of the bleak space. She explains that at sixteen her parents arranged a marriage for her. She was taken to Pakistan and married to a man ten years older. She met him for the first time on the day they were married. Once the ceremony was complete, the man returned with her to the UK and they moved in to his mother's house. Since then, she has been treated like a slave.

'What about your family?' Lisa asks Asha. 'Would they help you if you told them what was happening?'

'My brothers would kill him if I told them what he does to me. They would go to prison and it would be all my fault. My parents could not take me back, they would be shamed by me, I can't do that to them.'

'What does he do to you – your husband?'

'I cook and clean. If I don't do it as he likes, or if I'm slow, or sick, or tired, he will beat me. Sometimes with his hands, sometimes with shoes or a stick he keeps behind the kitchen door. Always on my back. She beats me too, his mother, but she always uses the stick. She says she doesn't want to get her hands dirty by touching me. It doesn't matter how hard I try – I just can't be good enough.'

Lisa reaches for Asha's hands, which are writhing on the table between them, and covers them with her own. Asha meets her eyes and continues.

'Every day I must be a wife to him – do everything a wife

is supposed to.' She stops, holding her gaze, long enough
to make sure that Lisa knows exactly what she means. A
shiver runs up Lisa's back. 'When he's done, he complains
about how disgusting I am, that he is cursed with an ugly
wife. He is an ugly man. But I am married to him – what
can I do? I am not allowed to take birth control and I am
terrified that I will get pregnant. Every time – after – I wash
myself with scalding water, even inside. I managed to get
some pills from the doctor but they have run out now and
they will not let me go back to the doctor. I cannot get pregnant. I will kill myself if I do.'

Asha begins to sob.

Lisa lowers her voice, trying to soften it, as if the razor-
sharp meaning of the words she has to say will cut less if
she speaks them gently.

'You've been forced to marry him, it's not arranged – it's
forced. Do you understand that?'

A nod through the tears.

'And what he does to you, when he forces you to do your
wifely duties, that's – I'm sorry to say it so bluntly – but
that's rape. We can arrest him for that.'

Asha shakes her head violently.

'I won't go to court. You don't understand. If he goes to
prison, his family will kill me. Everyone will hate me! I'm
supposed to do what I'm told – I'm supposed to obey. A
wife is supposed to obey her husband.'

'Not in this country.' Lisa says it with force. 'That is not
the law here, Asha, you do not have to live with this.' Lisa
knows how difficult it is for Asha, how entrenched her fear

is. Forced marriage is being exposed much more frequently than it used to be, but a huge part of it is still hidden within those communities that have learnt not to trust the police. The figures reported in the newspapers that tell the public forced marriage is a problem are only the tip of the iceberg. Entrapped women who are brave enough to report this abuse genuinely fear for their lives.

'No, no.' Asha pulls away, and Lisa can tell she is losing her again as the woman looks to the clock on the wall.

'Wait,' Lisa says, 'wait. I'm not going to force you to do anything, okay?'

Asha is shaking her head and grabbing at the bags of shopping around her feet.

'Asha, stop – look at me.' Asha looks up, and Lisa ploughs on. 'We can figure this out. I can help you.' She hears the words coming out of her mouth and her brain scrambles to catch up. She's making promises to this woman that she may not be able to keep. *How can we help her if she won't go on record?* Lisa racks her brain, thinking back through everything they've discussed, a possibility flickering to life in the back of her mind.

'You said he's from Pakistan?' Lisa asks. 'What's his immigration status here? Do you know?'

Asha lets go of the shopping bags and straightens in her chair. 'I'm the only one who can read and write English in that house. His visa has expired, but I haven't told him.'

Hope surges through Lisa, the flicker of an idea bursting into a full flame. 'We may be able to use that. Asha, please, give me his name and let me look into this. I can talk to Immigration.'

Lisa waits, hardly breathing, as Asha considers. Finally, after a moment that can only have been seconds but felt like hours, Asha nods and tells Lisa his name.

'I will not tell you the address. You cannot come there. If you find it, and you come there, I am as good as dead. Please.'

Lisa shakes her head. 'We won't come, we won't. I'm keeping this very close to my chest, I'm not telling anyone, nothing is going on record. No one knows.' Lisa wonders if she's saying the right thing. She doesn't want to break Asha's trust. She feels a prickle of fear at what she's promising. What if she fails? What if she gets disciplined for not following the rules – for not immediately reporting this to her seniors?

Asha takes a final look at the clock. 'I have to go. I'm in danger every minute I'm here. Every time I walk through those doors.'

Lisa knows that it will only take one person to see Asha coming or going from the police station and they will lose everything.

'Listen, I can meet you next time. At the market? I can wear normal clothes and meet you somewhere. No one will know that I'm police. Then you won't have to risk coming here.'

Asha nods, heaving her bags from the floor as Lisa opens the door for her.

'By the fruit seller, the one with the orange sign.'

'I know the one. Same time next week?'

Lisa watches as Asha leaves, waiting a couple of minutes before following her out of the doors and looking around. There is no one on the street. Lisa lets out the breath that she doesn't realize she's been holding.

Monday, 10 a.m.

The market is busy. Lisa picks up a cut-price packet of cotton-wool balls and pretends to read the label, whilst keeping an eye on the fruit and veg stall. She scans up and down the road, and finally catches a glimpse of Asha's face, gaze locked on to the fruit stall, arms full of bags as usual. Lisa jumps as someone speaks loudly nearby.

'You gonna buy them or just cuddle 'em all day?' The owner of the stall has appeared, looming over the assorted goods.

'Sorry,' she says, putting the cotton balls back on the table and smiling sweetly, 'sensitive skin.'

The vendor tuts as Lisa turns and slowly ambles towards Asha.

By the time Lisa reaches the stall, Asha is feeling some mangoes, her small hands nimble across the fruit. Lisa stands next to her, taking a paper bag from the stall and taking her time to select some kiwi fruits. She doesn't eat kiwi fruits, hates the feel of their furry skin, but they're the closest thing to her.

'I think I've thought of a plan.' Lisa keeps her eyes on the kiwis and her voice low.

In the last week, Lisa has made a lot of phone calls. She's spoken to the Home Office and Immigration, as well as one of her favourite inspectors, Sue Cohen. Lisa is trying not to focus on the fact that she's not exactly keeping her sergeant in the loop on this one. She pushes her worries about breaking the rules to the back of her mind. *Get Asha out. Worry about the consequences later.*

Sue has twenty-five years of experience in the force and is one of the leading experts on honour-based abuse in Yorkshire Police Service. They'd discussed the case one lunchtime in the canteen . . .

'So,' Sue had summarized, placing another chip in her mouth and talking whilst she chewed, 'she's living in hell, treated like a slave. She can't be seen to leave voluntarily, or to betray her husband, or she faces extreme violence from him, his family, or even possibly her own family. She won't go to court, or even on the record. She refuses to go to a hostel as she's convinced they'll find her, which frankly they probably would, if past experiences are anything to go by.' More chips went in. Lisa had looked at Sue's strong and wiry frame, thinking that if she went through chips like Sue did, she'd be the size of a house. Nearing fifty, Sue could still give some of the young'uns a run for their money. 'You remember that case last year, the nineteen-year-old?'

Lisa nods. 'Priya.'

Sue swallows, gulping from a bottle of water. 'Killed by

her own parents, buried in the cellar. That was another forced marriage. Her crime, obviously, was leaving a husband who she didn't love – didn't even know!'

'I dealt with another the year before,' Lisa adds. 'We managed to get her out. Sent her to a refuge way out of town. She was eighteen and they were taking her to Pakistan to get married, but of course that's not what she wanted. We hid her, it was only me who knew where she'd gone and it's a good job, because that family did everything they could to find her. Her father and brothers turned up in the station office, shouting and raging, the father insisting we told him where his daughter was. I told him straight – *she's an adult and it's her decision, I'm not telling you anything*.'

Lisa leans across the table and glances around, motioning for Sue to lean in. Heads together, Lisa continues in a lower voice, 'D'you remember that race relations officer that got sacked over the West Side not long ago?'

Sue nods.

'Well, he was this girl's uncle.' Sue raises an eyebrow. 'Oh yes, and guess who calls me one day trying to get information?'

'No.' Sue shakes her head in disbelief.

'Yes.' Lisa is angry now, recalling the way the girl's uncle had spoken to her on the phone. 'Giving it the big *I am*. He told me he was aware of the family and gave it the old sob story – they were a decent, loving family who just wanted their daughter back. Didn't mention that he was her uncle, of course, but she was a clever girl and she'd already told me all about him. She even said that he'd probably try and use his influence as the race relations officer to try and find her. Lucky it was me who took that phone call because this guy was convincing as hell. Told me that it was his job to know where she was so he could safeguard her, told me I wasn't doing my job properly for not telling him. Well, I kept refusing and he eventually hung up, threatening to take it to my superiors. Except I got there first. I wrote a statement about his behaviour for our commander, who took it directly to *his* commander.'

'Nice one.' Sue grins.

'Fucking cheek of it.' Lisa tuts. 'But back to Asha. The Home Office has confirmed that his visa has expired. But she can't be seen to be the one to report him for that – she's the only one who can read English in the house and she'll immediately get the blame if Immigration turn up. Apparently, he's not living at the address they've got registered for him, as they've already made enquiries there, and Asha is still refusing to tell us where she lives.'

'You know there's an argument here for having her followed.'

'I know.' Lisa nods, before shaking her head. 'But I just don't think it's the right thing to do. We've got to think outside the box with this one. We need to forget about prosecutions and investigations and just think about Asha. What's best for Asha? What does Asha need?'

'Freedom,' Sue answers.

'Exactly. If we can get him to voluntarily leave the country, he won't be allowed back in. Problem is, if he leaves, he'll take her with him. She'll be in even more danger in Pakistan. I just can't see a way to make this work.'

They had sat in silence for a few minutes, both staring into the middle distance. Then Lisa had stabbed the air with a finger. 'I think I've got it.'

Sue holds up a hand. 'You know the drill. Don't tell anyone you don't have to tell. Don't write anything down. You can keep this girl safe. You can give her freedom.'

Lisa knows what they are doing is off-book. In fact, she feels like she's chucked the book out the window, smashing the glass on the way. If she reports this, policies and supervisors would appear, her idea would be drowned in red tape and partner agency agreements before she could even formulate it. She knows for a fact that her sergeant, Tony, wouldn't approve of her spending this much time on Asha.

'I think you're right.' Lisa stands up quickly, the legs of her canteen chair screeching loudly across the laminate flooring.

'I'm always right,' Sue smirks, and then taps Lisa on the back of the hand, 'and you're doing the right thing.'

Lisa laughs lightly. 'So why do I feel like I'm flying by the seat of my pants, in a clapped-out helicopter, with no brakes?'

''Tis the nature of the job . . .'

The market-stall owner starts to shout about apples and pears and Lisa is snapped back to the present. She glances around to make sure no one else is within earshot before putting the idea to Asha.

'If he leaves the country, he won't be able to get back in.'

Asha's hands pause over the mangoes.

'Can you find an excuse to visit Pakistan? If you suggest it to him, will he go for it?'

'I don't know.'

'Think about it,' Lisa mutters, before adding, 'and don't forget that any time you want to leave, we can get you out. Any time.'

'Thank you, I know.'

Lisa knew as she said it that Asha could never leave with him and his family right behind her. She looks at Asha's heavy bags.

'I wish I could carry some weight for you.'

Asha turns to face Lisa for a quick second, smiling sadly. 'You already are.'

The last Monday

Lisa's nails are bitten to the quick.

She perches in her office, not settled enough to lean back in the chair, aware that in a couple of minutes she'll be on her feet – pacing – again. The phone rings and she jumps up, before registering the number on the display – it's a colleague's extension and won't be for her. She walks over to the window and looks out, flicking her hands in and out of her pockets. *What's happening? Is it all going to plan? Why haven't they called yet?*

Lisa had seen Asha eight more times since the day she'd bought a bag of kiwis she'd never eat. They'd sat in the office until they went soft and someone chucked them in the bin. On most occasions, Asha had slipped in the side entrance of the police station, Lisa standing ready at 10 a.m., ear to the door for Asha's timid knock. The doorway was down a side street, away from the busy thoroughfare of the public entrance, mostly used by officers beginning and ending their shifts. Asha had become more relaxed with Lisa – had begun to trust her – and showed Lisa some of the injuries that covered her body. Lisa noted finger-mark bruising around the tops of her arms. Long flat welts on her back from a stick. An old scald that had scarred over her right forearm and pinch bruising from her mother-in-law's cruel fingers. Lisa had instantly wanted to photograph them as evidence, but Asha had refused.

Twice more, they'd met in the market, but it wasn't possible for Asha to relax for a moment out in public, and they struggled to make any real progress in those meetings. On one occasion, Lisa had been about to approach Asha when a group of older ladies surrounded her, shouting greetings, poking and prodding at her, asking how she was eating, how was that tall husband of hers, was she feeding him well? Asha had turned from Lisa in an instant, and Lisa had slunk back into the crowd. For the rest of that week, Lisa was unsure if the women had been a coincidence, or a deliberate interception. She was racked with worry that they'd been seen, that Asha had been clocked coming from the station, that the women had been sent to take her away from Lisa. Worried that she'd never see her again.

But the following Monday, Asha turned up, explaining that the women were the matriarchs of her community, that they'd heard she'd be travelling to Pakistan soon and they wanted to pass orders and messages to their loved ones back home. This was the plan that they'd hatched together. That first day at the market, when Lisa had put the idea of getting Asha's husband out of the country into her head, Asha had begun to work on the plan from her side. If she could convince her husband to take her to Pakistan, then Lisa promised she could do the rest. There was no point in asking him or his mother directly; if they thought she had wanted to go to Pakistan then they would have done everything in their power to refuse the idea. Instead, Asha had gone to her mother. Holding back the full truth, she had shared a tiny fraction of her marriage woes, hinting that her husband seemed unsatisfied, that maybe he missed his homeland. She'd lamented that she longed to make him happy, but that despite cooking his favourite dishes from Pakistan, he remained sullen. She'd made it feel like her mother's idea, not hers. Their wedding anniversary was coming up, and her family insisted they would treat them to a pair of tickets home. The flights were booked, and Asha passed all the details to Lisa. She'd cried when her husband had shown her the tickets, saying that she didn't want to go to Pakistan. He had called her an ungrateful woman, and took pleasure in reminding her about the trip every day since, not realizing that it had been her idea all along.

Lisa walks back to her seat, checking her watch. The flight was due to leave at 13.20 and her watch says 13.37. She'd given strict instructions that she was to be called as soon as Asha was safe. *Why haven't they called?* Once Asha had given Lisa the flight details it was a fight against time to get everything sorted. Whilst hoping the husband would agree to fly, Lisa had made contacts with airport police at all the major airports. She'd kept it loose, discussing Asha's case as if it were a training exercise – *if I did want to do this, who would I need to speak to?* She'd got names and numbers and written them in the back of her notebook. She'd used Sue's name – *authorized by Inspector Cohen* – in one instance when a receptionist got a little shirty about giving out details. She hoped Sue would forgive her. She'd made many of her phone calls from her mobile, in the car, avoiding the office, and Tony, as much as possible. At that early stage, she hadn't been sure where they would fly from, or when, and she needed names and numbers for when the time came. She'd spent a lot of time on the phone. Once she knew the airport, she had dialled airport police and explained the situation.

'Essentially, what you're saying is, we need him to fly to Pakistan without her. But it's doubtful that he'll get on the plane if she doesn't.' Sergeant Brown, of the airport's police unit, had made a low humming sound as he considered all the angles. To Lisa's relief, he'd instantly understood the urgency of the situation.

'He definitely won't get on that flight if she's not with him,' she confirms.

'Okay, so we have to get them both on the plane.'

'Yes,' Lisa agreed, 'but it can't take off with her on it.'

'So, we get them both on, then somehow get her off the plane, without him kicking up a fuss, or following her, and send him to Pakistan on his own?'

'That's the plan,' Lisa replied.

'We'll have to deal with her bag, of course. They won't take off if her bag is on the plane and she isn't.'

Lisa had taken a deep breath and tried not to focus on all the things that could go wrong. 'Can it be done?'

Silence at the other end.

'It's a shitload of hoops to jump through. And each hoop will have to be lined up at exactly the right time, and everyone will have to know just when to jump through.' Lisa heard the sound of Sergeant Brown sucking the air in through his teeth. 'We're talking check-in staff, bag handlers, air marshals, the flight team – even the pilots.'

'This needs to work,' Lisa pressed, 'this is literally her only chance.'

'I'll come back to you.'

Lisa had begrudgingly ended the call, worried about the prospect of having to trust someone she'd never met. She had chewed her lip whilst considering that she'd just taken a stranger into her confidence. Into Asha's confidence. She hoped that Sergeant Brown had the sense to keep the information she had given him on a need-to-know basis, and cursed herself for not making that clear enough.

Now, pacing once again, Lisa tries not to let her heart sink at the realization of just how many people they were relying on. The plan had been made, and Lisa goes through it again in her head whilst she waits for the elusive phone call. The couple would check in their suitcases. Asha's suitcase would be removed from the conveyor belt before it got anywhere near the aeroplane, and placed in customer services for airport police to collect. Their seats would be moved to the back of the plane, so that Asha's husband would have no view of what was going on when Asha was called to the front. The flight team would wait until the absolute last minute, just before the doors were closed for take-off, and then make an announcement asking for Asha to bring her boarding pass to the front of the plane. Asha would explain to her husband, as casually as possible, that she had to have her boarding pass checked again. This was a critical stage of the plan. If Asha's husband followed her to the front of the plane, all would be lost. If he was present when they tried to remove her from the plane then he would insist on going with her, and they would be back to square one. The whole plan hinged on him letting her go to the front alone.

Lisa fiddles with a pen, trying not to imagine the worst-case scenario. She sees Asha, head low, sitting in a taxi on the way back to her husband's house, she sees his anger towards Asha, sees him berating her for mixing up the tickets, grabbing her physically, his hard fingers digging into the soft flesh of Asha's arms. Visions of the bruises Lisa had seen on Asha's upper arms threaten to overwhelm her.

Finally, the phone rings.

Lisa is waiting in the front office. She stands up as she sees Asha come through the doors, flanked by a taxi driver carrying her suitcase. Lisa is stunned by how different she looks. Despite still being dressed in the same dowdy, cheap clothes, she is totally transformed. Gone are the dark circles around her eyes and she holds her head high instead of stopping and hiding. She beams at Lisa, like a light has been switched on inside her, and they embrace. Lisa can feel Asha's heart pounding in her chest as the woman starts to bounce on her feet, and they both begin to bounce together, until they are jumping up and down like teenagers who just got the last teen idol concert tickets.

'It worked!' Asha cries. 'I can't believe it worked!'

'We did it!' Lisa laughs, remembering that she's a police officer in uniform but not quite being able to quash her delight.

Asha stops jumping and takes Lisa's shoulders. '*You* have done it. You have saved me. I can't believe he's gone.'

'And he won't be coming back.' Lisa grins.

Asha is incandescent with joy. She can't thank Lisa enough and it takes them a long time to say goodbye. Lisa has secured her a place in a women's refuge outside of town. A handy aspect of the plan was that Asha was able to openly pack all of the things she needed, and is therefore totally ready to go. She shares with Lisa that she hopes to return to her family in the future. Now that her husband has gone back to Pakistan, she won't be blamed for leaving him, and will be able to be honest about how he was treating her, without the fear of her brothers doing something stupid.

Lisa had made sure to inform Immigration that his visa had expired and asked them to put a note on his passport to that effect. This should ensure that if he ever tries to re-enter the UK he will be stopped before he can even board a plane. Lisa makes this clear to Asha, reassuring her.

As Lisa watches Asha walk away, head held high and shoulders back, she considers that she has nothing to show for this huge operation. There has been no official investigation. No crime report. No arrests. There'll be no debriefs or statistics to analyse, no commendations or pats on the back from the top brass. Despite all this, Lisa has never been prouder to be a police officer. As she walks slowly back to her office, smiling, she considers that police work is not always quantifiable. You can't calculate how much an officer cares. You can't measure how deeply a job affects them or how desperately they want to help someone. You certainly can't put a value on saving a life.

The easiest thing for her to have done, from the beginning of all of this, would have been to find out where Asha was living and go and arrest her husband and his family. In fact, she realizes, as she looks around at the other officers in her unit, that's exactly what many of her colleagues would have done. But Lisa had *listened* to Asha. Arresting all concerned would have ripped Asha's life apart. Lisa had thought outside the box, she had reached out to colleagues in different forces, to airport staff, police and air marshals, and they'd worked together. A bit of creative thinking had meant that Asha's life was changed for the better.

Lisa was off the streets for over a year. After her neck had completely recovered, she transferred to an area that had a less diverse population and returned to full duties. Due to her experience in honour-based crimes, Lisa was responsible for raising awareness of the issue to senior officers and departments in her new borough. She served in the Yorkshire Police Service for a total of thirty years. She rose to the rank of Chief Inspector. How police forces respond to reports of domestic abuse and forced marriage has changed significantly for the better since this incident occurred. Legislation has also been implemented to protect victims and give the police more powers to protect those who are subjected to domestic abuse and honour-based abuse.

Chapter 3

The question of what makes a person truly evil has been asked since we discovered that psychopathic serial killers exist. Are monsters born, or created? The debate of nature versus nurture is a theme that intrinsically weaves itself through fictional Sergeant Catherine Cawood's life in *Happy Valley*. Grandmother to Ryan, the son of convicted socio-path Tommy Lee Royce, she is constantly alert to the possibility that her beloved boy may turn out just like his dad. So present in her mind is the question above, that she asks it in the very first episode of the show. We follow Ryan's story throughout the TV drama, each of us asking the same thing. Do bad dads always create bad sons?

Police officers across Yorkshire are used to dealing with youths that have started their criminal escapades early. It's often frustrating for them to deal with the same faces, day in, day out, watching as young boys get sent to court time and again, only to be given slap after slap on the wrist. Many officers haven't the patience to work with young offenders. These are the officers that think children who start nicking things at ten years old are lost causes, no-hopers – destined for prison.

But some officers are born for the role. They have the unending faith – often incorrectly mistaken for naivety – that everyone can change, given the right support. They believe that monsters aren't born but made. That any child is worthy of support. They can look at a thirteen-year-old boy accused of burglary and still see a child. It's a gift that PC Ashleigh Sugrue put to good use during her years working with the troubled youths of Yorkshire.

Ten years old

A housing estate on the outskirts of a Yorkshire city. PC Ashleigh Sugrue steps into the front garden of the Walker home. The sound of mopeds and quad bikes roaring along the streets behind her grates on her nerves, like the mocking *you can't catch us* theme tune of the estate.

She raps on the door loudly, looking over the front garden as she does so. Colourful potted plants line the border, surrounding a small patch of bright-green grass. So green it must be fake. Compared to the Walkers' direct neighbours', in which sits a stained old sofa, next to a rusted car on bricks, this frontage is well looked after. That'd be the house the papers would get a photo of, she thinks to herself, as heavy footsteps sound inside.

Frank Walker opens the door. He's a tall, wide man with a cockney accent that slips into Jamaican slang when he's really riled up. Ashleigh has come to know him quite well in her role as a youth offending officer.

'Hey, Ash,' he says, with friendly resignation.

'Is Ricky in?' she asks, as Frank offers her a cuppa.

'No chance,' Frank says, shaking his head, 'probably him you can hear on that bloody quad.'

Despite living on the outskirts of a Yorkshire city for the last seven years, Frank has resisted even the hint of a Yorkshire lilt. He nods for Ashleigh to go through to the sitting room, where his wife Liz is sitting on the sofa.

'How are you today, Liz?'

Liz pats the seat beside her and Ash obliges. She's updating Ash on her recent operation when Frank walks in with the drinks. He's placed them all on a floral tray with milk, sugar and proper teacups, just as Ash's mother used to do. She smiles, taking in the juxtaposition of his prison tattoos and the delicate way he places a cup and saucer in front of her.

'I'm glad Ricky's out, actually,' Ash starts, 'as I wanted to talk to you about a couple more allegations of antisocial behaviour that've come in from local residents.'

Frank snorts, lowering himself into a chair. 'Antisocial behaviour? You wanna see how the rest of the kids on this estate behave! Ricky was seven when we moved here – you know I wanted a fresh start after being locked up – I wanted a better life for them. He was seven and a lovely lad. It's the bleeding *local residents* that set him on this path.'

'You know what they call 'em, don't you?' Liz cuts in. 'What the people in this bloody hellhole call our kids? *Half-caste, mixed breeds*.' Her lips curl angrily. 'I thought it was bad in London thirty years ago when me and Frank got together, thought it was bad then, but London's got nothing on this place.'

'I'm so sorry, both of you.'

He's shaking his head. 'What do they expect? Treat 'em like animals.'

'We can report racist remarks. I'm happy to look into it for you if you tell me who—'

Frank cuts her off with a wave of his hand. 'We ain't grasses. I've dealt with it myself and I'll keep dealing with it.' He cracks his knuckles together and Liz puts a hand on his arm, as if to say, remember who you're talking to.

At that moment a skinny boy walks into the room. He's got something wrapped up in a blanket and Ash can see how precious this bundle is by the slow way he is walking, not taking his eyes from his cargo. He stops next to Ash and says, 'D'ya wanna see my puppy?'

'The puppy belongs to all of us, Harry,' Liz says kindly. Then she adds to Ash in a lower voice, 'He's been getting a little possessive, bless him.'

Ash smiles at Harry as he proudly opens the blanket, revealing a tiny bundle of fur.

'Oh, my goodness, what a lovely doggy,' Ash says. 'And how old are you, then? Old enough to look after it really well, I bet.'

'I'm ten,' he says.

It's nearly home time and Ash is back at the office, the image of the little boy and the puppy in her mind as she thinks about Ricky. He'd eventually turned up home just as she was leaving, and Harry had run to him, jumping up almost as if he was a puppy himself, desperate for his big brother's attention. Ricky had dropped a packet of sweets on his brother's head, tickling him behind the ears as the boy laughed. Ash had looked at the packet of jelly sweets and known for certain that they would have been nicked from the corner shop on Ricky's way home, but in the spirit of supporting the family she'd stayed silent.

Her role is within the neighbourhood policing unit, specifically working with partner agencies such as social services, schools and the like, to create new and innovative ways of trying to set young offenders back on the right track. She's been working with Ricky for over a year now, since he was thirteen, but he just doesn't want to know. The fact that he has a supportive family that actually bothers to interact with her is a novelty. Most of the parents she has to deal with don't care what their kids are up to, so long as they're out of the way. She's been sworn at more by parents than by the young offenders themselves. She's glad Frank is on her side, although she can't help thinking that his past is repeating itself in Ricky. She had researched his criminal record before meeting the family for the first time. He's been inside for burglary and assault, and was part of a fairly notorious London gang during his teenage years. After his last – and longest – stint in prison, Liz threatened to leave him. She took the kids and left. He swore he'd turn his life around, suggested they move out of London for the kids' benefit, and here they were. As far as she knew, Frank had kept his nose clean ever since.

When she'd seen him today, she could tell he was desperate for his boys to take a different path than he did. Unfortunately, Ash believes that it's too late for Ricky. She was told last week by the burglary squad that he's about to get fingered on DNA for a couple of burglaries on the other side of the city. It's likely that he'll get a custodial sentence. She couldn't mention it to the family earlier that morning in case it got back to Ricky, giving him the chance to get rid of any evidence or stolen property he may be holding on to. She sighs as she logs out of her computer and picks up her handbag, feeling sorry for Frank and Liz. She wonders why she doesn't have the same sympathy for Ricky, then reminds herself that it's probably because he's a cocky little bastard whenever she attempts to talk to him.

As she heads for the door, she wonders when she lost her compassion, and promises herself she'll do better tomorrow.

Eleven

The lanky kid runs straight into her chest and she staggers backwards, taking his weight through her legs, and gripping on to one of his arms for dear life. The object he is carrying drops to the floor and smashes, sending silver and copper coins exploding outwards across the pavement like the bouquet of a firework.

'Gerrof me! Gerrof!' the boy shouts, as Ash regains her composure and takes him by the shoulders. He's not putting much fight into it, his bark much worse than his bite. She looks down into his face and her heart sinks.

Harry Walker.

A red-faced, rotund lady has followed Harry out of the laundrette and is shouting at him, the blue fronds of the mop she is waving poking at him through the air.

'Alright, alright!' Ash shouts, shocking the woman into silence.

The boy is still, and she wraps a hand firmly round his upper arm and marches him towards the shop. 'Let's talk about this inside, shall we?' A crowd of ten or so youths and passers-by has gathered on the street around them, and Ash is keen to avoid the camera phones and jeers as quickly as possible.

'He's not coming back in here!' The woman crosses her arms and blocks the doorframe. 'This is the second time this week. I didn't bother calling you lot the first time as you've got more important things to deal with, I expect, but this is ridiculous now.' Her nostrils flare at Harry as she finishes her rant with an angry nod.

'Okay, my love, I've got him now. Why don't you pop back inside and we'll get all this cleaned up for you – have you got a brush 'n' pan in there?'

The woman retreats into the soapy air of the laundrette and Ash turns to Harry.

'You're Frank's boy, aren't you? Harry Walker? What the hell have you done this for?'

Harry shrugs. He has the same glint in his eye as his brother, the same handsome bone structure of his father.

'Come on now, how's that dog of yours? Do you remember you showed me him when he was a puppy?'

'We called him Biscuit,' Harry says.

'I'll tell you what we're going to do, Harry. You're going to clean this up and then I'm going to take you home to your dad. Understood?'

He nods, and she lets go of his arm. He straightens his tracksuit top and crosses his arms. Satisfied that he's staying put, Ash turns back to the laundrette as the red-faced woman brings out a dustpan and brush. She hears a squeak of rubber behind her and spins back to Harry, only to find that he is sprinting away from her.

'Oi, you little git!' she shouts after him. 'I know where you live!'

She stands there, open-mouthed, as he disappears across the field. She turns to the laundrette owner, who's looking at her as if she should be giving chase.

'I'll catch up with him, don't you worry.'

'Well, who's going to clean up all this mess, then? I've got customers.' The woman raises an eyebrow at Ash.

Sighing again, Ash reaches for the brush.

Back at the nick, back aching from bending over, picking stray coins off the pavement, Ash searches the police intelligence systems and crime reports for Harry's name. She's disappointed to find a ream of reports where he's named as the suspect. Shoplifting, petty theft, breach of the peace, fighting and assault. His older brother Ricky had been sent to a Young Offender Institution a few months ago, but it obviously hadn't been soon enough. Ash knows the way it works. She's seen it time and again – younger brothers seeing the kudos their older brothers get on the streets for being 'bad boys'. She thinks back to last year, sees little Harry jumping around his brother. Of course, he wanted to follow in his footsteps.

And then there's Dad. He says he's doing his best to keep his kids out of trouble but his eldest is locked up and his youngest's heading the same way. He may have turned over a new leaf but he's still got the reputation of being a hardman. All the boys would have to do is google their father's name and they'd see the life he used to live. There's a particular photo of him in the press. Ash has looked at it, tried to marry the kind and gentle man she's spent a lot of time talking to over the last couple of years with the criminal in the image. Dripping with gold medallions, holding up a fistful of cash. Once those sorts of photographs are out there, there's nothing you can do to get them taken down. The boys will have seen them. In a community that seems to hate them, why wouldn't Harry rebel?

She picks up the phone and dials the Walker home.

''Lo?' Liz picks up.

'Hi, Liz, it's Ash.'

'Oh, hello, love.'

'I ran into Harry earlier. Literally. Apparently he's been nicking the charity box out of the laundrette.'

A beat of silence.

'Liz, you there?'

'Yeah.' Liz's voice is low. 'I don't know what's going on with him, I really don't.'

Ash waits, wanting Liz to share.

'He's been out all hours recently, hanging around with a bad crowd, I imagine. Y'know Martin, the boy that Ricky was always hanging about with? Well, he's got a younger brother and I think that's who Harry's out with all the time.' Ash can hear the sound of the TV playing in the background as Liz talks. 'Honestly, you know we try, Ash. Frank's taken away his Xbox and threatened to take his phone if he keeps breaking curfew, but if he doesn't have his phone then we've got no way of tracking him. He left it here the other night after he snuck out and I was beside myself with worry – I had no idea where he was. I feel like locking him in the house but we can't do that, can we?'

'I know it's tough, Liz, it's not your fault.'

'Who else? It's what everybody thinks, I know they do.

Whose fault is it if not ours? Frank's done his best to turn his back on his past but it just seems to follow us wherever we go. They say nurture versus nature? Maybe it's just their nature. Maybe I was a fool for marrying that man in the first place.'

'It's tough for kids these days,' Ash says, especially on estates like yours – there's nothing to do, no one gives a shit about them, society doesn't care. Then there's the racism they've had to face. Of course they feel like outsiders. All you can do is keep being there for them. Keep trying.'

A dog starts barking in the background and the line dulls, as if Liz has covered the receiver with her hand. Ash hears muffled shouting.

When Liz comes back on the line, the barking has stopped. 'Sorry, Ash, that bloody dog!'

'I remember meeting him when he was just a cute little puppy.'

'Well, he's not cute any more, bloody barking all the time and shitting all over the garden. Harry's lost all interest, of course.' She tuts.

'How's he doing at school?'

'Y'know, that's what I don't understand. He was doing so well. Good grades – better than me or his dad ever got – and he seemed to actually like it. Now he's bunking off and his grades are slipping.'

'It sounds like he definitely needs some intervention. Let's make an appointment for me to come round.' Ash flips open her diary and picks up a pen.

'Go on, then. But I can't guarantee he'll be here.'

Thirteen

Ash runs towards the crowd of kids in the middle of the street. A member of the public has called the police and reported a disturbance in the area. She'd looked around for a while before she'd heard the commotion and seen the crowd.

'Alright!' she shouts, arriving at the melee and giving it her loudest police voice. 'That's enough. Police! Break it up!'

Most of the kids scatter. Remaining in the centre are four or five teenagers, surrounding a small girl, who's sitting on the floor. Ash immediately sees a face she recognizes.

'Harry Walker. Why, when I am called to any kind of shit around this estate, is it always you I find?' She takes him by the arm, well used to his swift feet by now. 'Who's going to tell me what's gone on here, then?'

'She fell over,' Harry explains. 'We were helping her. Get off me, you mad woman.'

His mates laugh.

'A likely story,' Ash says, ignoring the riff-raff. 'Have they pushed you over, love? Have they taken anything?'

The girl shakes her head, eyes glued to her knee, which is bleeding heavily. Ash lets go of Harry's arm, deciding that she can't sort this out whilst holding on to him. She points at him. 'If you move, I'll make you regret it. I doubt your dad wants to hear about you running from police again.'

Harry nods.

Ash pulls a bandage out of a small medical pouch on her kit belt and kneels down next to the girl, who must be about eight. She's still staring at her knee, and her hands are cupped together, holding something.

'Are you okay, love?' she asks. 'What's happened?'

'I fell over,' she says, looking up at the boys.

Ash leans closer to the girl, whispering in her ear, 'If they pushed you, you just need to give me a nod. You don't need to be scared of them.'

The girl's eyes widen and she shakes her head. 'No, really – I fell over and spilt my sweets.'

She opens her hands to reveal a pile of hard candy, pitted with gravel from the road. 'They were picking them up for me.'

Ash looks at the dirty sweets and realizes that she's jumped to conclusions. 'Well, you can't eat those.'

She examines the girl's knee. It'll need a good clean, and maybe a couple of butterfly stitches to close the wound. She unwraps the bandage and presses the padded section firmly over the gash, expert fingers wrapping it firmly in a matter of seconds. She winks at the girl. 'That's better, let's get you up.'

She takes the girl by the hands and slowly pulls her up, turning round to apologize to Harry for jumping in too hard.

He's gone.

'You've got to be sodding kidding me,' she mutters, as a shout from the nearby shop gets her attention.

'Here you go, love.' Harry hops out of the shop and ambles across the road, handing the girl a new packet of sweets. 'I was just about to get them for you, before this mad old woman attacked me.' He cocks his head at Ash.

'Enough of the old.' She allows herself a small smile. 'Now clear off whilst I get this one home.'

Fourteen

Ash looks at Harry's face. He's sitting on the hard plastic mattress of a custody cell bed. His eye is black and swollen and there's dried blood around his nostrils.

'Burglary.' She stands before him with her hands on her hips. 'Really?'

He smiles, eyes twinkling. 'I don't know what you're on about, PC Sugrue.'

'Oh, is that right?' She paces the cell. 'Let's see if this refreshes your memory, shall we? Police are called by a resident around three this morning, says that his neighbour's being attacked in his front garden. Police arrive, minutes later, to find you being held down by a very angry bloke who says he caught you in his house. He may have given you a good pasting in his efforts to detain you. Does that sound familiar?'

Harry examines his nails, taking his time. 'Well, now that you mention it.'

'Harry!' Ash exclaims. 'I don't get what's going on. Why have you done this? Why do you *keep doing this*?'

Harry shrugs.

Ash plonks herself down on the bed beside him. 'We were doing really well.'

'Were we?' Harry asks, his voice betraying him with a high squeak, flickering between child and man. He clears his throat. 'What's the point? This life was good enough for my dad. Look at him now, he's doing alright. Why should I go to school and follow the rules? No one gives a fuck about where I'm going.'

'You know that's not true,' Ash says. 'You know we all care where you're going. Why the hell would I be sitting here with you, in a cell that stinks of piss, if I didn't?'

'You really should get new cleaners.'

Ash laughs. They sit in silence for a moment.

'You know you could go to prison for this?' Ash asks. 'Is that really what you want?'

Harry's lips tremble, and he flattens them into a thin line. He shakes his head.

'I know you've been to see Ricky. I know you've seen what prison's done to him.'

'Yeah.' Harry laughs. 'He's hench!'

Ash looks at him. 'I mean up here.' She points to her temple.

The smile fades from Harry's face. 'Can you help me?'

'You know I'll do what I can. But it may be too late.'

Ash stands and walks to the door. 'Want a cuppa?'

'Five sugars, please.'

'You'll get what you're given.'

She pushes his cell door shut, jiggles the handle to make sure it's caught and walks towards the custody kitchen. She rolls her eyes as she goes; *five bloody sugars indeed.*

Fifteen

'I know I need to pull my socks up.'

Harry and Ash are sitting on a wooden bench outside courtroom six. They're both wearing suits; Harry's is slightly too big for him, a hand-me-down from Ricky. Youth court is designed to be less intimidating than adult court, hence no uniform for Ash. No one wears gowns or wigs, and overall, it's a more casual environment than adult court. The sentences, however, can be just as harsh.

Ash nods. 'You do.'

'I don't want to go inside.' He looks to Ash, imploring. 'I can't go inside, Ash.'

His knees are shaking. She looks at them and he pushes his hands down on top of them. 'Pins and needles,' he says, 'these benches.'

She knows he's trying to cover up his nerves. She imagines her son sitting here instead of Harry and her stomach twists.

'I'm gonna change. This is it. Once this is done, I'm staying home. I'm not missing any school, this is it. I just need them not to send me down.' He looks at her again, his eyes watery. 'What's going to happen? You've done this before – you must know?'

Ash sighs. 'I don't know what's going to happen. It's impossible to guess. But, Harry – you may have left it too late.'

He drops his head into his hands.

'Listen, even if you get a custodial sentence, it won't be

for long, I'm sure. We can deal with it. You can still make the changes you're talking about.'

He snorts, face still hidden in his hands. 'Yeah right. Once you've been inside, you're marked for life. Ricky says it's like people can smell it on you.'

Ash doesn't know what to say to that. Ricky had been released around two months ago, whilst Harry's offences were waiting to come to court. He'd come out of prison with a few stones of new muscle, a tattoo and a book full of contacts. Told his parents he'd been looking for jobs but no one would take him because of his convictions. Ash didn't think he had even looked. All prison had done for him was give him what looked like PTSD and an anger he hadn't had before. He was now firmly entrenched in the criminal networks of Yorkshire. The only positive thing to come out of his sentence was that he wasn't allowed on the estate any more and therefore couldn't live at home. His influence over Harry had weakened.

She looks at the skinny boy waiting to hear his fate. She wants to take his hand and reassure him, like she would her own son. But she can't. Of all the dealings she's had with him – and there've been many – he's always been calm with her. She knows that he's a good kid. She's given her professional advice to the CPS, and despite the fact that it got her shit from the other officers back in the nick, she recommended no custodial sentence. She wants them to give him one last chance. Convict him of burglary, slap a Criminal Behaviour Order on him and tell him this is it. If he breaches the order he's going down. She's been called a sap, a mug, it was even suggested that her compassion for the boy is why women shouldn't be in policing. She clenches her jaw as she thinks about the attitudes of some of her colleagues. She wonders why they work in Youth Offending at all, when they have no intention of making a difference.

She's about to try to reassure him some more when the doors to the waiting room swing open and Ricky walks in. Harry jumps up, leaping away from Ash like she's contagious. His chest puffs up and he swaggers towards Ricky, who slaps him on the back and pulls him into a hug. Ricky's brought two friends with him, and Ash recognizes their faces from the multiple police briefings they've appeared in. They're linked to organized crime. She tenses, sitting straighter, keeping them in the corner of her eye but not looking directly at them. The last thing she needs is a confrontation in the waiting room.

They gather round Harry and she can hear his voice, louder and deeper than it was when it was just the two of them.

'Fuck off!' He laughs. 'You know I don't give a shit.'

The men give a cheer and there's more back-slapping.

'I've teed up the lads inside, mate,' Ricky says, 'you'll be looked after.'

They begin to murmur between themselves and Ash takes out her phone, pretending to check her emails. She can hear some of what is being said.

'Who's that?' one of Ricky's friends asks. 'Plonk?'

'Yeah, some saddo who's trying to help me.' Harry laughs, putting the word *help* in air quotes.

'Don't trust the bitch,' Ricky murmurs, 'they're all out to fucking get us.'

'For real,' Harry says, laughing, and she can feel the group looking at her.

Ash recognizes the term *plonk* as a reference to a female police officer, but doesn't react. She focuses on keeping her expression completely blank as a wave of embarrassment threatens to redden her cheeks. She keeps her eyes on her phone – *do not blush, don't you dare fucking blush* – scrolling blindly through her inbox, feeling stupid that just minutes ago, she was feeling sorry for Harry.

The doors to courtroom six open and a clerk calls Harry's name. The case is about to begin.

She stands and walks towards the door, and is nearly there when Harry pushes past her, shoulders back and chest out, and struts into the court.

Frank and Liz are sat in the public gallery. Youth court is usually closed to the public but certain family members are allowed for support. The case has been heard. As soon as Harry had left Ricky and entered the court, he'd reverted back to the polite but cheeky Harry that Ash knows. He has pleaded guilty to two counts of burglary. Everyone has been called back into the courtroom and the judge is ready to hand down the sentence. Ash interlinks her fingers and squeezes her hands together in her lap. She's glad she saw the other side of Harry. It's reminded her of just how close he is to becoming exactly like his brother.

Out of the corner of her eye, Ash sees a detention

officer enter the court. He's carrying handcuffs. Her stomach drops and she looks to Frank to see if he's seen them too. He has. He meets her eyes for just a second, before lowering his head into his hands. Liz hasn't noticed the cuffs and is still looking, wide-eyed and hopeful, at the judge.

'I sentence you to twenty-four weeks, the first twelve to be spent in a Young Offenders Institution. You will be subject to a Criminal Behaviour Order for a year after your release.'

Harry lets out a wail. The misery of it rips through Ash's chest and she presses her hands to her mouth. He's instantly transformed in that moment from the fifteen-year-old who laughed at her outside court to the ten-year-old who was desperate to show her his puppy five years ago. Tears well in her eyes, as they stream down his face, and he starts shouting, 'Mum! Mum – please – Mum! Don't let them take me away!'

Liz is on her feet, Frank holding her as she leans towards Harry, arms outstretched. Her face is contorted into a silent scream.

'Mum!' Harry shouts, standing up as the detention officer, joined by a colleague, takes one of his arms and tries to apply the cuffs. 'No!' Harry twists his arms away from the officers and tries to resist, his neck straining towards his mother. His face is red and stained with tears, his eyes wide – the eyes of a frightened child, not a criminal.

'Take him away, officers,' booms the judge.

Harry is dragged from the courtroom.

Sixteen

Ash pulls up outside the Walker family home and turns off the engine. She sits for a few moments in the cooling car, gathering her thoughts. She hasn't seen Harry since the day he was taken to the Young Offenders Institution. He had spent his sixteenth birthday in prison.

. Thirteen weeks ago, after Harry was taken to the cells, she'd found his parents sitting on a bench just down the road from the courthouse. Liz was attempting to dry her eyes, Frank rubbing her back.

'I'm so sorry,' Ash had said, stopping in front of the bench.

'It's not your fault, love,' replied Frank, standing up and pulling her into an unexpected bear hug. 'You've always tried your best for our boys.'

He'd released her, dropping heavily back onto the bench.

'Oh, Liz,' Ash said, kneeling in front of her. 'He'll be alright in there, y'know. It's only twelve weeks. He promised me he'd get his head down after that – it's not too late to turn all this around. Once he's out, all he's got to do is abide by the CBO for a year, that's really important. Did you get a copy from the court?'

Frank held up a bundle of papers. 'It's in 'ere somewhere.'

'So, the main points.' Ash had stood up and begun to count on her fingers. 'He can't cause anyone harassment, alarm or distress, he's got to be in by nine p.m. to abide by curfew, he can't go in the areas highlighted on the map there, and he can't associate with the boys named in the order.'

'We'll do our best,' Frank said, looking both bewildered and exhausted.

'Promised he'd get his head down? Ha. We've heard it all before.' Liz gulped. 'Both of them in prison, both! What the hell have we done to deserve this?' She began to cry again.

'Come on, love.' Frank pulled Liz to her feet. 'Let's get you home.'

'I'll give you a lift,' Ash offered, nodding towards the side road where she'd parked her car.

'Yes, please, love. Parking's a nightmare round here so we came on the bus. Can't take her back like this.'

Slowly, Ash on one side of Liz and Frank on the other, they'd walked to the car.

Back in the present, Ash climbs out of the car. Frank had called her yesterday, saying that Harry was asking to see her. She'd arranged to meet him at home, after school this afternoon.

He answers the door quickly. She's surprised to see that he looks exactly the same. Ash doesn't know what she was expecting, twelve weeks is not a long time, but she's relieved. He nods her through to the sitting room and offers her tea.

'Five sugars?' he asks, a laugh in his voice.

Ash smiles. 'Just the one, thanks.'

Harry disappears towards the kitchen and Frank pops his head in. 'I'll be upstairs if you need me.'

Ash nods, pulls out her notebook and pen. Harry is back

quickly and he hands her tea in a mug, none of the careful flourish of his father. He sits opposite her in an armchair and leans forwards, elbows on his knees.

'I need your help. I never want to go in there again, Ash.' He rakes his hands through his hair. 'It was horrible, I can't do it again. I don't want to give up on myself. I want to change.' His face is pale and his eyes are red.

'Of course, I'll do what I can,' Ash says. 'But I can't do it for you. You know that. It has to come from you.' She points at him with her pen. 'You need to want it. You need to stay in school, you need to stay in this house, every night. Say no to your mates. Can you really do that?'

Harry nods hard. 'I'll do anything. Please.'

'Okay.' Ash pulls a pamphlet out of her bag. 'There's a youth centre called Flight, they're the other side of town but they're the best. They offer activities, counselling, courses, they can even sponsor people into apprenticeships.' She hands the leaflet to Harry, who looks at it with interest.

'I can take you along tomorrow,' Ash says, 'but places are limited, you have to commit to going, you can't just turn up when you like.'

'Yes, thank you. I'll go.'

'Excellent,' Ash says. 'Let's get your dad down here so we can tell him all about it, shall we?'

Harry scoots upstairs to get his dad, and Ash sips her tea, a small flame of hope flickering to life in her belly.

Ash opens Harry's file for what will be the last time. For the last six months, he's been attending Flight at least once a week. The last time she spoke to Frank and Liz, they confided that he'd broken curfew on a couple of occasions, but had mostly been in on time. They complained in a lighthearted way about his constant moaning, but acknowledged that it was hard being a teenager stuck indoors all the time. His grades had improved, but he was still being marked down for back-chatting the teachers. Ash had laughed when she'd heard that bit.

As she writes her closing report, she notes that he hasn't broken curfew and hasn't been picked up on the streets by police since he'd made her a cup of tea in his sitting room half a year ago. She regularly checks the crime reports and intelligence systems for his name, and is encouraged when she doesn't find anything new. As far as she knows, he is abiding by the rules of his Criminal Behaviour Order, and is no longer considered a 'problem youth'.

She signs the bottom of the discharge form and closes the file. She opens her spreadsheet and deletes his name from the list. She sits back in her seat and takes a moment to silently wish him good luck.

Twenty-five

'PC Ashleigh Sugrue.'

A voice from behind her in the supermarket, just as she is picking up a punnet of mushrooms. She turns around and comes face to face with a handsome young man; he's holding a tiny baby in his arms and a woman stands beside him.

'Harry?' Ash smiles in surprise.

He's beaming at her. 'I knew it was you,' he says, wrapping an arm around the woman next to him. 'Hannah, this is the plo— sorry, police officer – I told you about. Ash, this is my wife, and this,' he holds the baby up so she can see a chubby little face, 'is my daughter, Elizabeth.'

'Oh my goodness,' Ash says, 'you're married, and a father. How lovely.' She really means it. 'How is everything? I was so sorry to hear about your mum.'

Harry nods sadly. 'It's okay, we're all just glad that she didn't suffer too much at the end.'

'How's your dad?'

'Same as ever!' Harry brightens. 'He'll be happy to hear that I ran into you. The woman who turned my life around.' He looks to his wife. 'She's the reason I'm not in prison right now.'

Ash waves away his praise as Hannah smiles, taking Elizabeth as she starts to wriggle in Harry's arms.

He holds out a hand. 'Seriously, I want to thank you. I don't think I ever thanked you properly back then.'

Ash takes his outstretched hand. His grip is firm, but not forceful, a confident handshake. 'The apprenticeship you got me led to me working for a construction company. Been there seven years. I'm a supervisor.'

'That's incredible, well done. I always knew you'd turn out well.'

'Oh really?' Harry laughs. 'I didn't!'

They laugh together, Ash wanting to hug him. Baby

Elizabeth starts to grizzle and Harry makes an apologetic gesture. 'We'd best get her home for her feed.'

'No problem,' Ash says. 'Lovely to see you.'

The small family walk away. Ash stands with her basket and watches them go, a huge smile on her face. When you've spent years genuinely trying to make a difference, yet frequently feeling as if you're smacking your head against a brick wall, it's wonderful when someone confirms that you succeeded. You don't get many people who say thank you when you're a police officer, and she can count the *thank yous* she's had on one hand, but this one – from the boy she first met when he was ten years old – might be the best yet.

PC Ashleigh Sugrue served thirty-one years in the Yorkshire Police Service. She progressed upwards to the rank of Sergeant and worked in many different units, including emergency response, CID, Child Safeguarding and Neighbourhood Policing. She received two District Commander's Commendations for her dedication to problem solving within the Neighbourhood Policing Team. When asked to sum up her career she said, '*I worked with some amazing people and learnt so much. Working as a police officer shaped my entire life. I loved most of it. Would I do it again? No. Too much has changed.*'

Chapter 4

In *Happy Valley*, we see the brutal murder of PC Kirsten McAskill as Tommy Lee Royce deliberately reverses a Mini into her, at speed. Kirsten is killed almost instantly, leaving her distraught sergeant and team pulling themselves together, and set on finding her killers.

That's what police officers do. They hold it together. It's this same steady professionalism that female officers across Yorkshire display on a daily basis, even in the face of the incredible challenge of losing a colleague and friend.

Thankfully, in real-life policing, the murder of officers is much rarer than it is in TV drama. It's easy to forget that policemen and women put their lives at risk on a daily basis. According to the National Police Memorial Day organization, more than 4,000 police officers have been killed on duty since the role of Constable was created in 1750. Many of those deaths can be attributed to world wars and the more lawless times of forgotten history, but since the year 2000, two hundred and thirty-eight police officers have lost their lives on duty, or whilst travelling to or from their place of work. Those who lost their lives 'on-duty' met their deaths as a direct result of a crime, or whilst trying to prevent, respond to, stop or solve, a specific criminal act. Of those two hundred and thirty-eight officers, twenty-two were women. Eleven of those women were 'killed in the line of duty'. You can read their names on the dedication page of this book.

One of those women was Police Constable Sharon Beshenivsky. A mother, a friend, a colleague and a dedicated member of the West Yorkshire Police. She was fatally shot in the chest at point-blank range when responding to a panic alarm at a travel agent on Morley Street, central Bradford, in November 2005.

18 November 2005

PC Carmel Wilson is looking down the barrel of a gun. Her colleague, PC Sharon Beshenivsky, lies slumped before her on the pavement. The sound of a gunshot rings in her ears as she watches the barrel swing horizontally towards her. There's no time to react. Her eyes focus on the dark circle, the sights and sounds of the busy street fading into nothing.

She hears the second shot at almost the same time as she feels the bullet rip into her chest. She is thrown backwards, her torso spinning to the left until she is crouching, turned away from her attacker, who is now running from the scene. Staggering, and with a searing pain in her chest, she knows that she must not fall. She can't let herself hit the pavement. She has to get help.

Shock has taken her ability to see straight but she grasps for her radio, knowing that she needs to press her emergency button. A button that will send out a signal, a *code zero*, to every cop in the vicinity, that an officer is in danger. She keeps staggering to safety as her tingling fingers find their way across the top of her personal radio and press firmly into the soft rubber of the button. As her radio sounds a series of high-pitched bleeps, she knows she has just a few seconds of clear airway to give her message, and she croaks out her location, saying, 'Morley Street, code zero, Morley Street.' She knows that at the sound of her emergency button, officers all around will be jumping from their seats, running to their cars, pushing their accelerators to the floor in an effort to get to her. She finally allows herself to rest, and sags to the ground.

The cavalry are coming.

When PC Carmel Wilson set off to work that morning, she could never imagine the trauma and grief that lay ahead of her. Every police officer regularly considers the possibility that they may not make it home one day, but it's always a day in the distance, out of focus, a day they believe will

never come. She was working an early shift, starting at
7 a.m., and her partner for the day was 38-year-old PC
Sharon Beshenivsky, a new recruit, who'd only been serving with the West Yorkshire Police for nine months. Carmel
herself had only been a police officer for nineteen months,
but Sharon had spent the two years before she became a
fully-fledged constable as a community police officer, and
between them they felt confident that their shared life
experience would help them deal with most incidents that
could come their way.

Before joining the West Yorkshire Police as a community
support officer, Sharon had spent many years working as a
childminder. She and her husband, Paul, had five children
between them, two that they'd had together and three born
to previous relationships. Their household was a busy one,
but Sharon loved the hustle and bustle, the noise – and the
love – of a big, busy family. She'd always dreamed of joining the police, and was proud of herself for finally taking
the step to become a full-time police constable.

They'd been assigned 'Taskit' duties that day, which
meant patrolling problem crime areas in their police car.
They were nearing the end of their shift as they wound their
way through the streets of Bradford. Carmel was driving,
and smiled as she listened to Sharon excitedly talking about
her daughter's birthday party, which was arranged for that
afternoon. It was the day Sharon's daughter would turn four
years old, and she was looking forward to finishing her shift
and heading home to her family, full of the fun of party
preparations. As they were sitting at the traffic lights on

St Stephen's Road, shortly before 3.30 p.m., an emergency call came over the radio – an alarm had been set off at Universal Express, the local travel agent's.

No other units responded to the call, and despite being near the end of their shift, Carmel raised her radio to her lips and said, '2841, will attend, Bob.'

'*Thanks for that, C,*' came the reply from Bob, the control-room operator, who was using the familiar nickname that Carmel had been given by their team. One last call before the end of their shift. They were both hoping it would be a quick one. Responding to alarms was a standard call for police officers, and many were false alarms. Carmel activated the police car's flashing light, headlights and siren, and set off towards Morley Street.

The pair could not have known what lay ahead of them, that in the travel agent's they were on their way to, a terrifying scene was unfolding. The four members of staff working that day were also looking forward to clocking off. An ex-employee had popped in for a visit and the mood was relaxed as the group chatted as they worked. Shortly before 3 p.m., three men entered and began to enquire about tickets. The men brought an air of menace with them, the friendly atmosphere soured, and seconds later the men produced weapons – a large knife and a pistol – and crashed into the staff-only area by vaulting the main counter. The violent crew struck one staff member on the head with the gun and a knife was waved at them to keep them in line. A quick-thinking member of staff managed to press the emergency button to alert the police, which in turn started the chain of events that would tragically end Sharon's life.

Carmel silenced the sirens before they reached Morley Street, a tactic often used by police so as not to scare away any potential suspects if they remained on scene. She pulled up on the opposite side of the road to the travel agent's and radioed the control room again to tell them that she and Sharon had arrived. Sharon got out of the car first, and they were approached by two traffic wardens, who warned them that something wasn't right. Carmel heard a noise coming from the travel agent's and she and PC Sharon Beshenivsky began walking towards it. Nothing more than a stride separated them as they walked together towards the premises.

Sharon was walking slightly in front of Carmel as they approached the door of the travel agent's, Carmel bringing up the rear – a position that could so easily have been the reverse. At first, she couldn't see the door as Sharon was blocking her view. Sharon suddenly stopped, but Carmel continued to move towards her, unaware of the danger that had caused Sharon to freeze. Carmel moved forward until she could see two males in the doorway. One of the men was ahead, and his hand was out in front of him. Carmel had only a split second to register that his fingers were wrapped around the handle of a pistol, five to six inches in length, before she heard an almighty bang, a bang so loud that at first her mind couldn't even compute what it was.

Sharon was still in front of her, and Carmel looked to the back of Sharon's head as it tilted to the right, then flopped quickly to the left, as Sharon's arms fell limp at her sides. Carmel's vision was crystal clear as she watched Sharon's knees give way, bending to the left, as her body dropped straight down and collapsed into itself, onto the pavement. Time seemed to stand still whilst also stretching into infinity, and there was time to see every detail but also no time to move as Carmel saw the gun, watched as it spun through the air, muzzle turning towards her. The immense pain, rather than the sound of the shot, was the first thing that told her she had been hit. As the suspects fled the scene, she knew she had to get to safety, and more than that, she had to help her colleagues find the men who'd just killed Sharon.

When the first back-up, PC John Smith, got to Carmel, she had collapsed on the pavement. Despite the fact that she was coughing up blood and could in fact feel the blood running down her throat, the first thing she did was tell John, who had run the 800 yards from the police station to help her, to get out his pocket book and write down her words. Every word Carmel spoke came at the cost of searing, unbearable pain through her chest, as she tried to gasp enough air to fill her lungs. PC Smith later testified in court that Carmel was *spitting blood*, but nevertheless, she described the suspect who shot Sharon and herself as an *Asian male, black hair, black jacket, no glasses, around 5'8 to 5'10 tall*. Despite seeing the man for less than four seconds, Carmel was confident of what she had seen, and knew that time was of the essence. Her determination in the face of life-threatening injuries enabled her colleagues to immediately circulate descriptions of the suspects involved.

Despite being shot in the chest, PC Carmel Wilson spent only three days in hospital before returning home. Her first priority on being discharged was to give all the information she had to the lead investigator in Sharon's murder, Detective Superintendent Richard Robinson. He listened intently as she told him everything she could remember about the men who had robbed the travel agent's and killed her friend. At the time, Robinson had no idea of the task he was about to face. The investigation would span a massive eighteen years, and involve hundreds of hours of determined focus, international manhunts, and arranging extraditions from Somalia and Pakistan. It was discovered that the gang thought they could steal up to £100,000, as the travel agent's dealt in money transfers and currency exchange. However, on the day of the robbery there was very little cash on the property and the robbers only came away with just over £5,000.

Six men have since been convicted for offences connected to the murder of PC Sharon Beshenivsky. PC Carmel Wilson's testimony was critical in achieving each conviction. Muzzaker Shah, thought to be the ringleader of the six men who set out to rob Universal Express, is believed to be the man who pulled the trigger. Muzzaker Shah, Mustaf Jama and Yusuf Jama were the men who entered the travel agent's, and were convicted of murder, robbery and firearms offences, and sentenced to life, with a minimum tariff of thirty-five years in prison. Faisal Razzaq and Hassan Razzaq were convicted of manslaughter, robbery and firearms offences. Faisal was sentenced to life, with a minimum tariff of eleven years, and Hassan was sentenced to twenty years in prison. Faisal had driven one of the cars used in the robbery, and also acted as a lookout with Hassan. Raza Ul-Haq Aslam, who acted as a third lookout for the gang, was convicted of robbery and sentenced to eight years in prison. A seventh man, Piran Ditta Khan, suspected of being the mastermind behind the robbery, was arrested in Pakistan on 14 January 2020. At the time of writing, he is still awaiting extradition to the UK.

A memorial to the life of hero policewoman PC Sharon Beshenivsky can be found in Norfolk Gardens in Bradford, the city where she was born. In 2020, after the last member of the gang responsible for her murder was arrested, the family whose travel agency was targeted by the gang said that Sharon '*died protecting us and we'll be for ever grateful*'. Waqas Yousaf, whose family runs the Universal Express travel agent's said that Sharon's parents visit the shop every year, on the anniversary of their daughter's death, and lay flowers. Paul Beshenivsky, Sharon's husband, described her as his rock. Remembering the day that she was killed, he said, '*She* [their daughter] *waited excitedly for her mum to come home. When Sharon was late I knew something was wrong. It breaks my heart to think that I will never hear her infectious laugh again, to think she won't be here to see our children grow. The people who did this to Sharon are cowards. They took away my wife, but they also took away a wonderful mum, and the world is a darker place without her.'*

A week after Sharon's murder, hundreds of people attended a memorial service at Bradford's Centenary Square, observing a two-minute silence to show their respect for the fallen officer. Her funeral was held in January 2006 and more than four hundred police officers joined thousands of members of the public at Bradford Cathedral.

In 2009, PC Carmel Wilson was honoured with the Excel Award for Public Service in the Face of Personal Adversity, which recognized her determination to return to work as soon as she could after the shooting. She retired in 2023, after serving nineteen years on the streets of Bradford.

Chapter 5

We've seen from multiple real-world crime stories that some men will do anything to keep their secrets from being exposed, including murder.

When a man kills a woman to keep a secret, he is telling us that he values his reputation – what people think of him – over that woman's life. He is publicly showing the world that he cares more about being liked, than he does about erasing a woman.

Men who care more about themselves are dangerous, and have almost always got a long history of subjecting women to coercive control, verbal abuse and violence. There are many domestic murders that the police aren't able to prevent, despite increasing efforts each year – as we gain more and more insight into the lives and methods of abusers – to monitor and protect the victims of domestic abuse. When a murder can't be prevented, the police will try their hardest to bring the killer to justice. Working closely with them are forensics experts like Sarah Carling, whose eye for detail and perseverance has led her to solving the riddles of many domestic murders.

It's a Sunday morning and Sarah Carling stands on a Yorkshire moor. Her feet are firm on the edge of a roughly paved road that she has her back to. She is looking down onto a steep verge, where the scant smattering of snow and ice has been disturbed, the scrub flattened. Her gaze follows the pattern of disruption until it reaches the bottom of the verge. There stands a white crime scene tent.

As a crime scene investigator, Sarah has been called to forensicate the body of a woman that's been dumped on the moor. (Purists will tell you that there is no such word as *forensicate*. This is the term, however, that is in common use amongst police forces and forensic investigators.) It's bitter, and she's glad that she's wearing multiple layers of clothing under her crime scene suit. She looks across the landscape, usually picturesque, but grim today. Grey clouds hang low, rain a fine mist in the air, and she thinks of all the crime scene experts that have stood on the moors before her. There's a feeling about the place. The wind whips around the hood of her suit, plastering her face with a thin film of rain as she begins to side-step down the hill, avoiding the area of flattened scrubland. She has a heavy bag slung over her shoulder, a metal case in one hand and her clipboard in the other. She is careful where she places her feet, yet she still stumbles a couple of times before she reaches the tent, the weight of her scientific equipment threatening to pull her hard onto the icy mud.

She looks back at the way she's come, imagines somebody trying to carry a body down the steep slope. Considers again the flattened grass. *More likely parked at the top and rolled it down.* It has snowed in the last few days, but today the temperature has risen enough that the snow has turned to rain. She'll need to make sure someone photographs the path of disturbed ice before it melts completely. She pulls on a face mask and, pushing one of the entrance flaps aside, steps into the tent. A woman's body lies face up in the centre of the tent. Her short brown hair is wet and stuck to one side of her forehead and her eyes stare, sightless, in the direction of the sky. There is heavy bloodstaining around her hairline, and a visible concavity to her skull on the left side of her head. Sarah can see immediately that she's suffered a major head trauma. One leg is tucked under the other, bent at the knee, and her arms are splayed out on either side.

She is fully clothed, but not in anything suitable for the weather. A thin T-shirt and joggers, with ankle socks. No shoes. She looks fresh, but the temperature of the moors today is lower than the temperature of most refrigerators, and has been lower than 3 degrees Celsius for at least the last week. Sarah is aware that decomposition will have been slowed by the cold. It's not her job to find out how long the body has been here; that will be down to the pathologist, and instead she runs her eyes over the body, noting multiple spots of bloodstaining.

She looks to the woman standing next to the corpse, and smiles. 'Rosie.'

DCI Rosie Faulkner turns to Sarah, returning her smile. Her face is pale, with two high spots of red just visible above her mask, and Sarah wonders how long she's been out in the cold. Sarah places her heavy equipment on a small fold-out table that has been placed on one side of the tent, grateful to put it down. She's chosen to bring most of her kit, as the details on the scene were scant, and she didn't fancy scrabbling up and down the verge any more than she had to. She rolls her shoulders in wide circles as Rosie speaks.

'This, we're fairly certain, is Annika Hurley.'

Sarah nods. 'Went missing nine days ago?'

'That's right.' Rosie looks down at Annika's body. 'She's only twenty-five, was a trainee nurse. We're certain that somebody close to her has killed her. We're thinking the boyfriend, brother or father. They were the last three that saw her alive.'

'I saw them on her missing person's appeal. If the father did it, he's a damn good actor – those tears nearly made me cry.'

'I can't imagine a father doing this to his own daughter,' Rosie says, shaking her head, 'but then, men are capable of horrible things. The boyfriend has admitted rowing with her the day before she went missing.'

Sarah opens her clipboard. It's the thick type, with a lid, and a storage compartment for paper and pens. She pulls out a blank piece of paper and begins to sketch the scene within the tent, as well as the rough marks the body probably made as it rolled down the hill. She takes her time, first roughing out a sketch in which the space is captured. She will fill in more detail as she finds it. She's often asked to provide her sketches to the detectives who interview murder suspects, as the level of detail helps them formulate the questions they want to ask.

Until she gets on her knees and examines the body, she has no idea what her crucial evidence will be. She won't know what evidence could potentially crack the case until she's examined everything. She carefully steps around the body until she's standing near Annika's head. She lowers herself onto her haunches and examines the woman's face.

'So, potentially she's been out here for over a week.'

'Unfortunately, yes.' Rosie shifts on her feet, rubbing her hands together.

'We've lost a lot of definition in the bloodstaining,' Sarah says, looking at the layer of moisture that covers Annika's alabaster skin. 'Any spatter that was on her face will likely have been washed away. Same with the clothes, here.' She points to Annika's T-shirt, where large, dark-red patches cover the area of her left shoulder and upper chest. 'The moisture from the rain has soaked through any blood patterns here, causing them to diffuse. We'll bag the clothes and get them dried, but as she's been out in the elements for such a long time, the bloodstaining probably won't tell us much about how she was killed.'

'We need to find out where it happened. It clearly wasn't here.'

'No, she's just been dumped.' The bright lights that have been secured in the roof of the tent illuminate every blade of grass around the body. Sarah takes a long, slow look at the ground around her. No signs of bloodstaining. 'If he'd attacked her here there'd be blood everywhere. You know what head injuries are like, there'd be pools of it. This is a secondary scene. A dump site.'

'Will you take the clothing here, or leave it on her?'

Sarah considers the question. The most recent forensic practice, especially when attempting to preserve blood spatter, was to take the clothes from the victim at the scene, as soon as possible. This was because in previous cases, moving the body had been discovered to have caused the loss, or the shifting, of blood patterns on the clothing. The size and direction of blood spatter – a subject Sarah was passionate about – can give a forensic examiner invaluable information about the method of attack a victim has suffered.

'We'll take it here. Can't be too careful, there may be some small dry spots where the rain hasn't penetrated.'

A head pops through the tent flaps and Sarah's colleague, Jerry, says hello.

'Glad you're here, Jerry,' Sarah calls, as his head disappears again. 'It's a bit tight in here. Give me a few minutes with the chief, and then we'll get started.'

'I'll get out of your way,' Rosie says, edging towards the exit.

'Anything in particular I need to look out for?' Sarah asks, pen hovering over her notes.

'Not really,' Rosie says, putting her hands on her hips and leaning forward to stretch out her lower back. 'It's a bit of a tricky one. No obvious motive for any of the men who were with her last; her relationship seems to have been fairly healthy, her family have described her as a *daddy's girl*, so they've got a close relationship, it seems, and her brother seems like a well-rounded, normal young man. She apparently left home for work in the morning, nine days ago, but didn't arrive there, and then wasn't seen again. Her father reported her missing the day after.'

'Bit late, isn't it?'

'Not in this case, as she used to spend a few nights a week with her boyfriend. Her mum and dad just assumed she'd gone to his after work and was staying there. He rang them the next morning to check in with her as he hadn't been able to get in touch with her. That's when they found out she hadn't come back from work. They called the hospital and found out that she'd never turned up for her shift.'

'She's fully clothed, which could mean that the motive wasn't sexual.' Sarah looks at Annika. 'Are we worried about it being a stranger attack?'

'We're keeping an open mind, of course. But as you know, they're very rare. We've had mounted police out all around her address and the local area – you've probably

seen on the news – dogs, the helicopter, we've been stopping cars and showing them her photo. For over a week
now, found absolutely no trace of her, no sign of a struggle.
Not one witness has come forward to say they saw her after
that morning she was last at home. It's nearly always someone close to the victim.'

Sarah nods, thinking how sad it was that that was true.

'I'll head back to the nick,' Rosie says, stepping carefully
to the tent flaps.

'We'll be a good few hours here,' Sarah replies. 'You
should pop home and catch up on some sleep while
you can.'

Rosie laughs as she leaves the tent, as if going home to
sleep was the absolute last thing she could do.

Jerry enters a couple of seconds later.

'Right, J.' Sarah points to the equipment table. 'We're
going to tape her skin, hands and clothing first. Then we'll
take her clothing, need to get it over to the drying room as
soon as possible to try to preserve any staining that hasn't
been destroyed by the rain.'

'Sodding weather,' he says, quirking an eyebrow to
the sky.

'Indeed. Let's get going.'

Sarah stands in the workshop at the rear of the Hurley
household. There's a faint smell of cleaning products in the
air, the shelves are neatly stacked with tools and boxes.
It looks way tidier than any workshop Sarah has ever seen.
It's freshly cleaned and organized – not a spot of dust

anywhere – the rest of the house had been clean, but messy. Like you'd expect it to be if the residents had been going out of their minds for the last ten days.

Standing in the doorway she feels overwhelmed. Maybe it's the lack of sleep she's suffered since the investigation began, or the immense pressure she feels to get justice for Annika, but it feels like there's a lot of weight on her shoulders. She asks herself the question she's asked a million times before: *what if I miss something? What if I don't find the crucial bit of evidence that can give Annika justice, and her killer gets away with it?*

She closes her eyes, takes a deep breath through her nose and slowly exhales. She reminds herself that all she's doing is completing a jigsaw. She imagines tipping out the pieces and spreading them before her. It's an analogy she's used during CSI training many times before, to explain the role of a crime scene investigator: *think of a jigsaw. It's got a thousand pieces and you're going to try to build it without looking at the picture on the front of the box. You stare at the pile of pieces. They mean nothing. But you keep looking, and you see that a couple of pieces look the same. You gather those pieces together, finding more as you go, and you've built a door. Next, you build a dog, and then a tree, but you still can't see the full picture. It doesn't make sense. But you keep looking – putting similar pieces together until all of a sudden, you've got a picture of a house, with a dog sitting on the doorstep and a tree alongside. There may be a couple of pieces of the jigsaw that you can't find. Maybe you'll never find them, but you've built enough that you can interpret the picture, and what's happening in it.*

She opens her eyes. Just take it a step at a time. Find the pieces. The workshop is large and square, with mains electricity, insulation, windows and a sink in one corner. The floor is tiled. Harold obviously spends a lot of time in here. Sarah has her crime scene suit on and plastic booties cover her shoes. The family has chosen to go to a relative's house whilst the house is searched and forensicated. It's standard practice, in cases of murder, to examine all the places in which the victim has been. As well as the Hurley family home, Annika's boyfriend's – Richard's – place is also being examined, as well as his car, and the Hurley family car.

Sarah starts by simply looking. Really looking, observing the minutiae of every surface, working her way across the room. She begins with the floor. The tiles are terracotta, with grouting that could have once been white, but is now a light grey. She bends at the waist, so that her face is almost parallel with the floor, and walks slowly from the workshop door to the opposite end of the room, sweeping her gaze from left to right as she goes. The floor is clean, and it's really the grout she is looking at. It's notoriously difficult to get blood stains out of grouting. She's nearly at the end of the room when she sees it. A jolt of excitement zips through her chest, and she stops, bending her knees, bringing her face closer to the floor. There, in the grey grout between two red tiles, is a tiny fleck of blood. It can't be more than a millimetre wide. She stays absolutely still, still feeling the thrill of a discovery course through her, and lets her eyes adjust. She quickly spots another fleck, even tinier than the first, around three centimetres from it.

This is the part she loves. It reminds her of looking at the stars. You gaze up at the black sky, spotting a few bright points of light. Those are the closest stars, the ones your eyes can see easily. Then, your eyes relax, your gaze widens, and more, smaller stars begin to appear. The longer you lie there, the more stars you see. It happens as she continues to stare at the floor. More and more tiny specks appear. She takes a steadying breath as she realizes that she may have found the place where Annika was killed. Before she can be certain, she needs to test the spots to see if they are blood. She can only do a presumptive test on scene, and if the spots are shown as likely to be blood, then further testing can be done in the lab, to hopefully find DNA, and reveal if it's Annika's.

She takes a circle of filter paper from her kit and folds it to form a triangular point. She chooses one of the spots and rubs the tip of the paper across its surface. She then unfolds the circle of paper. A faint dark mark can now be seen in the centre, where the filter paper has picked up some of the red-brown substance from the grout. Next, she takes two small bottles and puts a few drops of the first liquid – leucomalachite green – onto the stain. This is followed by a few drops from the second bottle – hydrogen peroxide. If the sample she's collected is blood, the stain will glow turquoise.

The chemicals are quick to react, and in under a second,

she's looking at a bright turquoise reaction in the centre of the paper. Her heart pounds in her chest. *Blood*.

'Whoever's cleaned the workshop did a pretty shit job,' Sarah says into her phone, sitting in her car outside the Hurley household. She's got the engine running and the heat up. DCI Faulkner is back at the nick, and Sarah wants to relay her initial findings as soon as possible.

'Definitely a bloke, then,' Rosie quips. 'Are you telling me you've found our murder scene?'

'I think I have,' Sarah replies, hearing the eagerness in Rosie's voice. 'There's indications of blood spatter in the workshop, near to the sink in the corner at the back. It's low to the ground, and from the direction of the spatter I can initially estimate that she was lying with her head nearly under the sink. We know, of course, that the first blow won't produce spatter, so the blood that is present has come from the second blow and onwards. I can tell that there's been multiple blows; at least two of those are likely to have been delivered when she was already on the floor.'

Sarah looks at her detailed sketch of the scene. Each drop of blood hits the wall at a certain velocity, causing it to become tear-shaped, with a tail like a comet. The direction of the spatter can be followed back to the origin of the injury. She's drawn an estimation of where she believes Annika would have been lying when the fatal blows to her skull were delivered. It will all have to be put into a detailed statement for court, of course, but it's looking strong.

'There's also evidence of diluted blood in the sink,' she adds.

'He's washed his bloody hands,' Rosie says triumphantly.

'Looks like it.' Sarah had found haloes of diluted blood on the porcelain. When blood is diluted in water it doesn't just disappear. She smiles to herself, holding her cold fingers out to the hot-air vents, as she thinks just how much she bloody loves science. If a drop of water with diluted blood in it is dropped onto a smooth, hard surface, and allowed to dry, the blood will form a ring, or 'halo', around the outside of the drop. 'There's a row of plant pots behind the sink, on the windowsill. Someone has removed them and wiped down the sill, then replaced the pots. Lucky for us, they forgot to clean the pots themselves. I found diluted blood spatter on them, and I can tell that they've been moved for cleaning, as the position of the spatter has also shifted. If we can get DNA saying it's Annika's blood, it will be great evidence.'

'Fabulous,' Rosie says. 'You've found our crime scene, and we appear to have found a motive.'

'What have you discovered?'

'Her father, Harold, was having an affair.'

'Wow,' Sarah exclaims.

'I know. Apparently, it's been going on for over ten years.'

'*Ten years?*' says Sarah. 'Bloody hell! Did Annika know?'

'That's what we're trying to find out,' Rosie answers. 'If she did, and she confronted him, we could have our motive. He killed her to stop her exposing his secret. We'll be taking him into custody as soon as possible.'

'It's honestly horrifying that men would rather kill a woman than let her expose him,' Sarah says, feeling an exhaustion wash over her.

'Tell me about it. Should be unbelievable, yet happens time and time again.'

'Fucking men,' Sarah mutters.

'Fucking men,' Rosie agrees, as someone calls her name in the background. 'Gotta go, see you back here in a bit.'

Rosie hangs up, and Sarah sits in her car, staring through her windscreen at the normal-looking house before her. A family home, well maintained, cared for. A neat front garden. Nothing to indicate the horror that has happened within. With a sigh – partly of satisfaction and partly of sorrow for Annika – she switches on her engine and drives away.

Harold Hurley has been arrested on suspicion of murder. Sarah stands in the forensic garage and looks at his car. She's been told to examine it as a priority, so that anything found can be put to Harold in interview. She's cleared the main body of the vehicle and has paused for a cup of tea. She takes a loud slurp as Jerry approaches her. He has been examining the vehicle with her.

'Enjoying that, are you?'

'I would've made you one, but you didn't answer when I yelled.'

'Yeah, yeah.' He laughs. 'No worries.' He begins to make a coffee, flicking on the kettle before turning back to her. 'Bit disappointing so far.'

'Yeah,' she agrees, leaning against the small kitchen worktop that they have in one corner of the garage. It's separated from the main floor by a stud wall with a large Perspex window. Preparing food and drink in the same room as you examine a car wouldn't be the done thing, and Sarah has discarded her suit and gloves for her break. She nods to the car. 'We've still got the boot.'

'I know where I'd put a body,' Jerry says, 'and it wouldn't be up the front with me.'

'I always get excited when we get to a boot,' Sarah admits.

'Heard you had a look at his glasses and shoes earlier?'

'Oh yes.' She nods, swallowing another gulp of tea. 'I could see a faint red mist across the glasses, so I've asked the lab to prioritize those.'

'I don't get how people can just walk around with blood on their glasses without noticing.'

'You'd get it if you wore them,' she says, pushing her own glasses up with a middle finger, 'mine are always absolutely filthy. Your eyes adjust to it. It's only when you take them off to clean them that you realize how dirty they are, you put them back on and everything looks clearer.'

'But surely if you'd just murdered someone?'

'Yeah, but what do I do before I get in the shower? Take my glasses off. They never get washed, and if you're like me, and wear them from the moment you wake till the moment you sleep, they rarely leave your face.' She finishes her tea and rinses out her cup. 'Anyway, the blood from the kitchen has been confirmed to be Annika's. If we can find spray on his glasses then we prove he was there when she was killed. If we find blood in the car, we prove he took her to the moor. Problem is, they think – from the blood patterns on the clothing – that she may have been wrapped in a stiff fabric – maybe like a rug or carpet – at some point.'

Jerry makes a hmmm sound as he stirs sugar into his coffee. 'So he may have wrapped her well enough to stop any blood transferring to the car.'

'Judging by the shit job he did of cleaning the workshop, I'm hoping not.'

'Nice,' Jerry says, with a sour chuckle. 'Off you go, then, don't let me stop you.'

She smiles at him, knowing that he knows; she wants to do the boot herself.

Sarah gets suited up again and begins examining the inside of the boot. The inner felt is a navy colour, and she's grateful that it's not black. Blood will be easier to spot. She starts at the bottom and works her way up, taking tape samples as she works, to pick up any fibres that may have transferred from the body to the boot. She can't see any signs of blood. She knows that Annika would have bled heavily – the pathologist has determined blood loss and blunt force trauma as the cause of death – so where is it all? How has he managed to get her to the moor, if not in his car?

Her heart begins to sink after she's been working for an hour. She moves on to the underside of the parcel shelf, the last place to examine. Jerry has come over to see how she's doing, and her heart stops as she sees a familiar pattern of dark-coloured dots across the navy-blue felt.

'Jerry, look!'. He leans over her shoulder to where she's pointing, the noise of his paper suit crumpling in her ear.

'Blood spatter does it again.'

'But why? Why is there spatter in here? Has he hit her again whilst she's in the boot?'

'Can't be – there'd be much more if that was the case.'

'Agreed,' she says. 'Maybe it's some other kind of transfer. There's absolutely nothing in the rest of the boot.'

'Well, if she was wrapped in fabric . . .' Jerry ponders, rubbing his chin through his mask.

'Mmm,' she says, puzzled, 'I'll need to have a think about this one.'

She photographs the spots and tests them. Once again, the filter paper colours turquoise. She takes detailed notes of their positions and maps out the direction they have flown from. She knows that this is a spatter pattern, but it's small, a very light transfer.

Once she's done, she stores her notes and stretches her back. There's a lot of bending involved with scene examination. She pulls off her protective clothing and as she's changing, her mind goes back to that day on the moor. She sees the white tent and Annika's staring eyes. She feels the bitter gale of the moor and a light bulb goes off in her mind. She remembers the direction of the wind, imagining where Harold's car would have been parked. She grabs her notebook, scribbling furiously.

*

'DCI Faulkner.' Rosie answers the phone after only two rings.

'Rosie, it's Sarah.' She's sitting in the small office area of the forensic garage.

'Hey, love.' Rosie's voice is warm. 'What have you got for me?'

'We've found blood spatter in the boot.'

'Fucking yes,' Rosie exclaims, a sharp bang in the background, that Sarah imagines is Rosie slamming her fist on her desk in satisfaction.

'It's only a small amount, and I was confused at first, but I think I've got a theory.'

'Go on, Wonder Woman.'

Sarah waves away the compliment, even though Rosie can't see her. 'So, bear with me on this. I couldn't work out why there was a small patch of spatter on the underside of the parcel shelf, especially when there was nothing in the rest of the boot.' She finds herself rushing her words, desperate to get the information out, to make it make sense, and she deliberately slows herself down. 'Harold would likely have parked at the top of the verge where we found Annika. Do you remember how windy it was up on the moor? Well, I've checked the wind speed and direction for the nine days before we found her, and it was windy all week. The wind in our spot was west to east. Let's imagine that Annika's body is wrapped in thick fabric. If that's the case, there's likely to be a lot of wet blood inside it, unable to dry, or escape. Harold parks facing north, opens the boot, reaching in to lift her out, and a flap of the fabric comes loose, slapping in the wind. This causes the gathered droplets of blood to fly through the air, west to east, and land on the underside of the parcel shelf, as the boot is open. The direction of the spatter I found would back up this theory.'

'It's brilliant,' Rosie says. 'Honestly, Sarah, excellent work. So now we've got the spray on the glasses, and this. We can put him at the scene and dumping the body.'

'What's he said in interview?'

'He was denying everything, until we told him that we'd found Annika's blood in his workshop.'

'As per,' says Sarah.

'Exactly. Once he knew we'd found the scene, he gives us this story about Annika being moody that morning. Honestly – the way he talks about his own daughter – he said that she kept "pushing his buttons" and that she shoved him. He said he pushed her back, causing her to fall and hit her head.'

'Right,' Sarah says, sarcastic.

'He insists that Annika didn't know about the affair. However, his story doesn't match up with the boyfriend's – Richard – or Annika's mother's. Richard told us that Annika had been upset, for some time now, about the way her father was treating her mother. Apparently, he would go out for hours on his own, and never told them where he was. He would spend money on himself and his hobbies, or socializing with his mates, but he would never take her mother out or treat her to anything. Richard said that the *day before* Annika went missing, she told him that she had found some romantic getaway brochures. She knew they couldn't be for her mother. She asked Richard if he thought her father was having an affair. He told her he did.'

'So, she did know about it.'

'She at least suspected. Annika's mother also said that Harold came home two hours later than he said he had, on the evening she went missing. A neighbour backed up her timings.'

'He's been caught in a hell of a lot of lies.'

'And, of course, his story kept on changing. After he was confronted with the forensic evidence showing he'd struck Annika with something, he changed it again. He now claims that Annika was being abusive to him over the affair, that she was swearing at him, that he retaliated, calling her an *ungrateful little bitch* and lost control. He's said he grabbed a large spanner and "struck out" with it. He denies repeatedly hitting her whilst she was on the floor, but has admitted wrapping her body in some old sacking and putting it into the boot. He said he drove around for hours before leaving her body on the moors. When the detective asked him why he hadn't told the truth in the beginning, he said he felt like he'd had a "mental breakdown" after he dumped her body, causing him to forget everything he did.'

'He'll be trying to get off on insanity, or a crime of passion?'

'Probably. We'll have to see what he says in court,' Rosie answers, the sound of a yawn in her voice. 'But basically, thank you . . . if you hadn't found the blood – in the work-shop, the car.'

'I'm so glad I did,' Sarah cuts in before Rosie can compliment her any more. 'This is literally why I do what I do.'

'Well, I, for one, am glad you do it so well.'

Three hours was all it took the jury to find Harold Hurley guilty of the murder of his daughter, Annika. His defence attempted to offer on his behalf a guilty admission to the crime of manslaughter, but this was rejected by the judge. In his summing-up, the judge condemned Harold for trying to suggest that his violent attack on Annika was triggered by something she said or did. He was sentenced to life in prison. DCI Rosie Faulkner still believes that the success of this case was down to the tireless work of CSI Sarah Carling, whose work on the murder scenes was fundamental to the securing of a guilty verdict.

Forensic Scientist Sarah Carling has spent over forty-five years working on many thousands of criminal cases across the Yorkshire region. Her work has included a wide range of cases, including break-ins, road traffic collisions and serious sexual assaults. Sarah's preferred area of expertise, and the area that she is internationally recognized for, is her work on the investigations of violent assaults and murders. She is passionate about the analysis of blood-spatter evidence, believing that it can provide unparalleled insight into the methods murderers use to kill their victims.

Starting at the lowest scientific grade, she rose up through the ranks, gaining various qualifications along the way, to become the most senior-grade casework scientist, with responsibility for all other government-employed, scene-attending, forensic scientists. She now delivers training to scene-attending police officers and scientists both in the UK and abroad.

When asked to sum up her impressive career, Sarah said, *'I recognize how lucky I have been to work in a job that I have loved from day one. I started straight from school, not knowing what to expect. During my first week at the laboratory, a senior member of staff said to me, "You do know that you have come into a man's job?" Although this made me uncomfortable at the time, he did not realize that his comment made me all the more determined to succeed.'*

Chapter 6

In the TV drama *Happy Valley*, when Winnie, Catherine
Cawood's kindly elderly neighbour, bravely steps forward
to protect a vulnerable victim of human trafficking, she
asks Catherine why the police can't just arrest the leaders of
the notorious crime gang responsible. The Knezevic
brothers are referred to mysteriously throughout the series,
and we never really get a grip of everything they get up to,
but it's clear that they are responsible for countless violent
incidents throughout Catherine's valley.

The legends of real-life gangsters also haunt the corri-
dors of real Yorkshire police stations, where their names are
mentioned, but few officers really know the full story. Most
see the leaders of organized crime gangs as untouchable,

slippery figures, who have an uncanny ability to escape justice time and again. Huge investigations, involving hundreds of thousands of pounds and countless officer hours, are undertaken frequently, all across the UK, to try to chop off the heads of these organized crime gangs, which are known as OCGs. Each investigation involves the examination and capture of the gang's members, who are sent out to commit crime and earn money and kudos for the gang.

The Organized Crime Unit is responsible for making its communities safer from the danger posed by serious and organized crime, leading the fight against OCGs across the region. Carjackings and high-value burglaries are the bread-and-butter offences of many crime gangs, and DC Elizabeth Squire is well versed in bringing violent, organized criminals to justice.

Victim 1

Amy clasps her hands tightly around a polystyrene cup as she talks. Each time she lets go of it her hands begin to violently shake. Though the cup is empty, DC Liz Squire can tell that Amy is hanging on to it for dear life.

'You're doing really well, Amy,' Liz says with an encouraging smile.

The two women are sitting in a 'soft' interview room, designed to put victims or vulnerable witnesses at ease. Their conversation is being recorded for evidential purposes. Amy sits on a two-seater sofa, a cushion on her lap, hands clasped around the cup resting on top of it. Liz sits in front of her, slightly to one side, in a plush-looking armchair. A low coffee table stands between them, with a large box of tissues in the centre.

Amy is twenty-three. Small and slim, she's only five feet tall. She's wearing skinny jeans and a hooded sweatshirt. She has a sling on her right arm and butterfly stitches over a one-inch cut on her forehead, just above her right eye.

'Just tell me what happened, from start to finish, in your own words.'

Amy nods, squeezing her eyes shut for a moment, before speaking. 'I was at the lights on the high street. I think it was about five p.m. I was on my way home from work, the radio was on. It had just started spitting and I was fiddling with my wipers when the passenger door suddenly opened. I jumped in shock, there was this man there, he's like in my car in a second, and then he points this knife . . .' Amy pauses as she begins to cry.

Liz takes a tissue from the box and hands it to Amy, who covers her nose and mouth with it and continues to sob.

'Take your time,' Liz soothes, 'there's no rush. I know this is upsetting, thank you for doing this.'

'He's pointing this knife at me, shouting.' Amy talks through gulps, her voice thick with spittle. 'I couldn't hear what he was saying – I was so scared – I just froze.'

Liz remains silent. She wants Amy to talk, uninterrupted. To get everything out. Something she says may lead to a break in the hunt for the dangerous men that have done this to her.

'Then the door opens next to me – the driver's door – and all I feel is someone grab me round the arm and yank me out of the car. I felt like I just flew backwards, like they pulled me *so hard* I didn't have time to brace myself or anything before I hit the road.' She raises her left hand to her head injury and touches it gently. 'I don't know whether I hit my head on the car door or the tarmac, but I felt really dizzy and sick, with fear – you know?'

Liz nods encouragingly.

'All I wanted to do was get away from that knife. I didn't care about my bloody car! All my stuff – I was upset afterwards, about losing my handbag, wallet, phone, you know – but right then? It was just the knife. I just had to get away from the knife.

'I started crawling backwards, like shuffling. I was trying to stand up but my arms and legs were like jelly. I couldn't feel any pain, I think the shock was numbing me.'

'How's your arm now?'

'Still a bit sore, but they don't think there'll be any long-term damage – fingers crossed. I didn't feel it at all until the men had driven off in my Astra. Once that woman came to help me. She tried to lift me up and I just screamed in pain. She told me it was dislocated.'

'Yes,' Liz glances briefly at her notes, 'she was a nurse, I believe.'

'You know when you imagine these things happening to you? You think, what would I do? I always thought I would shout – fight – do something, you know? But I just sat there. They could have done anything to me. I have dreams that they kept me in the car, took me with them. That they wouldn't let me go. I think about it all the time, what could have happened.' Amy begins to cry again.

'You did absolutely nothing wrong,' Liz says, pushing the box of tissues towards Amy. 'The fact that you're here, giving evidence, is incredibly brave. No one knows how they're going to react when something awful happens to them.'

'I can't see them again. I won't have to see them – in court – will I?' A look of panic crosses Amy's face, as if she's just considered the reality of what she's doing, the reality that she may end up giving evidence.

'We can protect you in court, we can use screens. They won't be able to see you during your evidence. You'll be able to use separate entrance doors and areas of the court, you won't be near them at any time.' Liz feels desperate to reassure her, she can't lose this witness. 'We really appreciate you coming in, we already have one suspect in custody and I'm sure we'll find the other one soon. We're hoping that we'll be able to remand them both to prison until the court case. All going well.'

Liz is careful not to make any guarantees. She knows how many cases don't even make it to court in the first place and doesn't want to make promises she can't keep. She's seen the look of disappointment in too many victims' eyes.

'I know you've given descriptions before, but can you tell me as much as you can remember about the men who did this?'

'I didn't see much of the second one, the one who yanked me out of the car.'

'That's fine, anything you can remember could be useful.'

'The first one, he was white, but maybe, like, Italian or Spanish or something? Quite tanned. He was clean-shaven, except a tiny goatee thing, like an arrow pointing down, under his lip. He had his hood up – it was dark blue, I think. I don't know what he was wearing on his lower half, as soon as I saw the knife, I just blanked everything else out. I remember the knife had a red handle. It looked like a kitchen knife, you know, the thick ones, like for cutting meat?'

'What did he sound like? Any accent?'

'He was local, Yorkshire. I remember his eyes were huge, really scary-looking, and he had a tattoo on his neck, but I couldn't see what it was.'

'What side?'

Amy tilts her head and closes her eyes. 'Left.'

Liz notes everything down. 'Anything at all on the second guy?'

'He had something over his nose and mouth, I think, but I could see he was white. That's pretty much it. He was in all black, or dark, clothes.'

'Could you tell how tall he was? What was his build like – thin? Fat?'

'I was on the floor when I saw him, I couldn't tell you at all. He wasn't fat, kind of average size? The other guy had quite a thin face, his cheekbones were quite sharp, but no idea how tall he was as I didn't see him till he was sitting next to me with the knife.'

Victim 2

'I can't believe I managed to get a photo of them.'

Liz smiles widely at Graham, a local farmer. He's sixty-one years old, and had been disturbed last night by the sounds of gunshots near his farm.

'It's amazing, honestly, Graham. Excellent evidence.'

'Glad to help. These louts need locking up. Christ, firing a shotgun willy-nilly in the middle of nowhere, could've got someone killed.'

'We can clearly see the passenger in the photo you took, and we've arrested a suspect already. Obviously, the driver was slightly quicker.' Liz hands a printout of the photo to Graham. It captures the full face of the startled man in the passenger seat, but the driver has lifted his arm up, leaving only a small portion of his forehead visible. 'Is there anything else you can tell us about him?'

'He had bleached hair, really white, like, in a big puff on top of his head, blue eyes. I shone my torch right in his face,' Graham says with satisfaction. 'He pulled up his hood right quick but I saw his hair first!'

'That's brilliant, Graham, thank you.'

'My grandkids won't believe it – I tell you – they're always laughing at me for being slow on my phone.' He chuckles, shaking his head.

'So, what led you to leave your house yesterday evening?'

'I heard gunshots.' He sits forward a bit, letting out a grunt as he moves. 'I've been a farmer all me life, I know what a shotgun sounds like. Sounded like it was close. When I looked out the window I saw the lights of the red Astra – couldn't see it was red from there, of course.

'So, me and my lad – he's staying with us temporarily on account of marital issues – we head out towards the lights and we find these two oiks, revving the Astra.' He rubs the stubble on his chin, rolling his eyes. 'They're stuck in the mud, aren't they? Idiots!'

'What happened next?' Liz asks.

'Well, I've shouted at them, haven't I, told 'em to get off my farm, and that's when the driver has pointed the shot-gun at us.' The smile has dropped from Graham's lips. 'I pushed my lad away and we both turned to run – he fired at our backs. 'Appen God was looking out for us in that moment, because only He knows how we weren't killed.'

The colour drains from Graham's face. His hands are in fists, years of farmwork etched on them in thick, gnarly wrinkles. 'He was aiming for me and my lad.'

Liz watches the strong man in front of her, suddenly vulnerable, and thinks of her own father. She fights the urge to put a hand over Graham's hand. Too emotional.

'As we're running off, we can hear sirens, but they're not close and I wasn't sure if they were coming to help us or not. I heard the doors slamming and I was convinced they were chasing us.' He shakes his head, a little out of breath at his re-telling. 'I told Dan, my lad, to run ahead and call t'police. I can't run like I used to. Once he was ahead, I ducked by a bush to catch my breath.

'I could see them in the lights of the Astra, they'd left it running and were giving it long-legs across my field. The sirens must have spooked 'em. Anyway, it was only once I'd walked back to the house and taken my jacket off that I felt my back was wet. I realized they hadn't missed.'

A nurse appears at the end of Graham's bed and looks at Liz, raising an eyebrow. 'He needs his rest now.'

'I'm going,' Liz says to the nurse, before turning back to Graham. 'Thank you, Graham, you rest. I'll be speaking to you again soon. You've done wonderfully.'

'Oh, thank you, love.' Graham rests his head back against his hospital pillow and closes his eyes.

Victim 3

Liz sits in Tracey's pretty, floral sitting room. Tracey has just brought in a tray of tea, beautifully presented in decorative cups and saucers. Liz glances out of her sitting room and through to the front door, which is still boarded up with large sheets of chipboard. Despite being seventy-two, Tracey's hands are steady as she places the tray on the table.

'The forensics team were all very polite, lovely people,' she says, as she pours tea for Liz, 'and they tidied up everything when they were done, I was amazed! Not a trace of fingerprint dust remained. Very professional.'

'We'd be lost without them,' agrees Liz, taking her cup and saucer. 'This looks great, thank you, Tracey.'

She takes a tiny sip of the hot tea, enjoying the slight

scalding sensation at the back of her throat. She loves to drink her tea hot, though there's little opportunity in this job. 'We'll have to get a full statement from you in due course, Tracey, at the station in our special interview room. It's very cosy, and it will all be recorded, will that be okay?'

'Yes, of course,' Tracey says, nodding determinedly. 'These men need to be brought to justice.'

'I just wanted to come here today to get your initial account of what happened. I know you've spoken to the uniformed officers who were here last night, I'm afraid there's a lot of repeating yourself involved in providing statements.'

Tracey shakes her head. 'It's absolutely fine. I'm just glad you've caught them.'

'Well, we have one man in custody.'

'And I'm sure you'll get the other one soon. I honestly can't believe it, twenty-three years I've been here and nothing – *absolutely nothing* – like this has ever happened. I've always felt safe here. I've got my son-in-law staying over at the moment. He says he'll stay until I feel safe again, but honestly, how can I feel safe now?'

'I understand, it must have been such a shock,' Liz says. 'Where were you when they arrived?'

'I was in here, I'd just decided to head up to bed. I was switching off the telly when I heard a banging sound from the front door, then a huge smash.' Liz points to the front door, visible through the hallway from where they are sitting. 'I think I must have screamed, because I could hear a man shouting for me to shut up. I was almost too scared to

look, but I peeked at the door and saw it was all smashed
and there was this arm coming through, reaching about.'

'That must have been terrifying,' Liz says.

'It was! The first thing I thought, of course, was to call
the police. I usually have my phone in the cradle, here' –
she points to a cordless phone that is sitting in its charging
point, next to her chair – 'so I don't have to get up every
time it rings. I reached for it and realized I'd left it in the
kitchen. I can't tell you how hard I cursed myself then,
silly woman.

'I couldn't bear to cross the hallway to the kitchen, not
with that arm waving about.' Tracey picks up her teacup
and takes a sip. 'I shouted out, *the police are coming, I've
called them!* – but they were making such a racket that I
doubt they heard me. I realized that they weren't going to
give up until they got inside. I wondered whether I could
make it up to my bathroom and lock myself in. But then, I
thought, should I go for the phone instead? I didn't know
what to do.' Tracey has put down her tea and is wringing
her hands. 'I thought, if they get in here, they're going to kill
me. I thought about my children, about how awful it would
be for them to find me here, dead and beaten.'

'How awful for you,' Liz says, 'I'm so sorry.'

'Anyway,' Tracey sniffs, lifting her chin upwards as if to
shake off her fear, 'it went quiet all of a sudden. Then I hear
them shouting again. They said, *we only want the car,
throw out your keys.* I didn't believe them, plus my car keys
were hanging right by the door, you see – in the little key
cupboard?'

Liz looks at the little key safe that sits on the left-hand wall, just inside the door. 'I'm supposed to lock it, but I never do. What's the point of hanging your keys in a cupboard and then locking it with another key, which you then have to hang somewhere else?

'I couldn't move, couldn't even bring myself to think about getting anywhere near that door, and as I was frozen, wondering what to do, wondering if they really would leave if I could somehow get to the keys and throw them out, a great big gun comes through the hole in the door.' Tracey presses a hand to her chest. 'Everything exploded in sound, I've never heard anything so loud in my whole life. It sprung me to my feet and I was up those stairs like a whippet, locked myself in the bathroom and sat against the door. I sat there until the police officers arrived. I think I would have sat there all night if they hadn't shown up.'

'You didn't see either of the men?'

'No, just that bloody gun.' Tracey heaps a large spoonful of sugar into her tea and stirs vigorously, saying, 'Why the hell not? Bloody deserve it after all this.' She resumes her story. 'I heard what I thought was my car starting up and driving off, after I'd been in the bathroom for a few minutes. Then silence. I thought they'd probably gone, but then I couldn't shake the thought that they were tricking me. What if one of them had driven off, to trick me into coming out? I kept imagining a man, with that gun, creeping up the stairs towards me. I was petrified. And in my own home. Disgusting.'

'They are disgusting, these men – you're right.' Liz takes

another gulp of her tea. 'They don't care who gets hurt. So, they took your car, a Mini?'

'Yes.' Tracey nods sadly. 'I loved my little car.'

Suspect 1

'We've got a photo of you in the stolen Astra. Luckily, your victim had the presence of mind to take it, before you and your mate shot him in the back.'

'I didn't shoot no one.'

Liz pushes the photograph across the table and points at Lee Benson's face, clear as day, gormless, and lit up by Graham's flash.

'This is you, isn't it?'

'No comment.' Lee refuses to look at the photo.

'We can all see it's you. The jury will see it's you too, so why don't you tell us who you were with, and maybe the judge will look favourably on you when he hands down your sentence.'

'No comment.' Lee yawns loudly, not bothering to cover his mouth.

'Lee,' Liz says, looking at the young man before her. He's wearing a grey, standard-issue custody tracksuit, after his clothes were seized for evidence upon arrest. 'You're a young bloke, you don't want to spend the next twenty years in prison. You do realize that you've been arrested on suspicion of attempted murder?'

Lee stares at her, arms crossed. His solicitor sits beside

him, staring at the opposite wall. It's an hour into the interview, and Lee has clearly chosen to say nothing.

'You're lucky that the pellets from the shotgun you used mostly missed your victim, otherwise you'd be looking at a murder charge instead.'

'I never shot no one.'

Liz ignores the double negative and opens the file next to her. 'We'll move on from the photo, then. I put it to you that once you escaped from the Astra, that was stuck in the mud, you ran to a nearby house. You smashed in the front door of the house and recklessly shot the firearm into the ceiling, before taking the resident's Mini.'

'No comment.'

'Well, we found the Mini, Lee. It's being forensicated as we speak. I think we're going to find your fingerprints in there, Lee. You know why?' Lee stares at her, mouth firmly closed. 'Because in that photograph of you in the stolen Astra, you're not wearing any gloves, are you?'

'I wasn't in no Astra.'

Lee's solicitor glances at him, the first interest the man has shown in the interview.

'No comment,' Lee says.

Liz pushes three more photos across the table. 'We're also examining the Astra. In it, we found a can of lager' – she points to the first photo – 'a shotgun case and a black balaclava. None of those items belongs to the victim. They're currently at the forensics lab, being examined. Are we going to find your DNA, or fingerprints, on these items, Lee?'

'No comment.' Lee shifts in his chair and taps his fingers on the tabletop.

Liz can tell by the way he's started to fidget that she's making him nervous. 'I think we are,' she says, leaning forward. 'You know what else we found in there? The bank card of the woman who had her red Astra carjacked. So now we have proof of a link between the carjacking and the aggravated burglary. I think you were in both those stolen cars, and I think we're going to prove it. Why don't you tell us why you were there?'

'No comment.'

'Was it just a case of wrong place, wrong time? Did you not know that your mate had a gun?' Liz asks, before continuing when Lee again refuses to answer. 'Maybe you had no idea what he was planning to do that day, and once you were in you were too scared to try and stop him, is that it, Lee? Why don't you just tell us who the other guy is? You don't seem like the bad guy here. Was it him who brought the gun?'

'No comment.'

'Where did he get the gun, Lee?'

'No comment.'

'Who is he, Lee?'

'No comment.'

'If we've got this all wrong, Lee, just tell us. If you were somewhere else, if you've got an alibi, just let us know.'

Lee yawns widely again, shaking his head, and then tipping it back to look at the ceiling.

Liz hides her frustration at Lee's refusal to talk with a wide smile, and ends the interview. She's more than used to suspects going no comment. It seems to be the standard advice given by most solicitors – *say nothing until we know what they've got on you* – and many suspects refuse to give a defence until their day in court arrives, and they know that all the victims and witnesses have actually turned up. Liz remembers the excitement she used to feel when watching television detectives verbally sparring with cunning crooks and thinking, 'I'm going to do that one day,' fading to the disappointment of real-life interviews. If only.

Outside, she discusses the case with her DCI.

'We need the second suspect off the street. He's still got that bloody shotgun.'

'I know, guv,' Liz says, wiping her brow. 'We're working on it.'

Witness 1

PC Ben Thompson unclips his kit belt, places it on her desk and sits down in the seat she's offered him.

'Long shift?' Liz asks.

'Not too bad, so far,' he says, smiling. Liz looks at the young man: white, tall, crew cut, muscles, designer beard, neatly shaped – the stereotypical male police officer. He's got five years' service, Liz has checked.

'So, you've got some information on our carjacking?'

'Yeah.' He leans forward and rests his elbows on his knees. 'Sorry, I would've linked this sooner but I've just got back from four rest days and only just seen the carjacking suspect descriptions on the briefing.'

'No worries.' Liz waves his apology away, wanting to get to the point. 'What have you got?'

'So, about thirty minutes before the carjacking, I was on the high street. I'd just finished a shift and was walking to the pub with a couple of the lads. Anyway, I walk past these two blokes, they were hanging around outside the little shop there, you know, on the corner of the high street?'

'I know it.'

'I recognized one of them, but it took me a few seconds to register who it was. I looked back at them just to make sure it was him – and it was, I'm certain of it.'

'Who was it?'

'Jack Shaw. He's well known for gang crime, particularly aggravated burglaries and weapons offences. I've printed out a custody image for you.' Ben reaches into the pocket of his stab vest and pulls out a folded A4 sheet. 'They were acting shifty, looking about, hoods up, y'know.'

Liz nods, taking the sheet and unfolding it. She looks at the face of a white male, around twenty-five, with a large bouffant of bright-blonde hair on top of his head.

'He was with the goatee guy who fits the description of the other suspect. Once I saw the briefing today, I put two and two together.'

'This is amazing, thank you.' Liz stands, about to take the photo directly to her DCI. 'Can you get me a quick statement written about the sighting. Asap?'

Ben nods. 'It'll be a great excuse to have a cuppa.'

Liz smiles at Ben and thanks him again, before hurrying into the DCI's office.

'Guv.' Liz raps her knuckles on the open door. DCI Alexis King looks up from his desk.

'What you got?'

She fills him in on what PC Thompson has just told her, but she has more to update him on.

'Also, guv, I got a phone call from a burglary DC over the north-side. He reckons our two suspects are good for a spate of aggravated burglaries that they've been investigating. He'd seen the briefing about our suspect – Lee Benson – and reckoned he matched the description they had for their burglaries. When he looked at our crime scene photos, he recognized something. He thinks the shotgun case we found in the red Astra – the one taken in the carjacking – was from a shotgun that was stolen at an aggravated burglary a week ago.'

'So that's where they got the shotgun,' the DCI says.

'Looks like it, and this burglary was really nasty. Two suspects smash into a woman's house – she was alone – they've got machetes. They tie her up and hold her hostage for over an hour, whilst they ransack the house. The address was a farm, so of course they have a shotgun, it was her husband's – locked away in a cupboard, in its case. The same case – we think – that we found in the Astra. I was going to speak to the victim today to see if she can identify the gun case, but it looks like I'll be going to court to get an arrest warrant for Jack Shaw instead.'

'Absolutely.' DCI King nods. 'Get to it.'

Liz marches out of the DCI's office and starts to write up her grounds for an arrest warrant for their second suspect. There's no time to waste. Every second Jack Shaw is out there with a gun increases the chances that he'll kill someone.

Suspect 2

Liz stands outside Jack Shaw's house. It's 4.30 a.m. on a Saturday, and the residential street is dark and quiet. She looks at the team of armed police that are lined up outside Jack's door. She's not afraid to admit that she's glad he'll wake up with a shock.

Due to Shaw's previous history of firearms and violence, it's been decided that the armed police will force his door to effect entry as fast as possible. The fact that the firearm involved in the recent burglaries is still outstanding obviously increases the risk to all the officers involved. She's standing with two unarmed, uniformed officers. They will be the ones to arrest Shaw if he's in the house. This will leave Liz free to conduct a search along with the specialist search team she's arranged, who are still in the warmth of their minibus.

Liz flinches as the first boom of the metal battering ram echoes around the street. One is all it takes. Armed officers flow into the house like black lava, shouting *armed police!* and clearing the house room by room. She's not permitted to enter until the house is cleared. It only takes a few minutes for Shaw to be found in bed. The rest of the house is empty.

The sergeant in charge of the armed unit clears Liz to enter.

Jack Shaw is in a T-shirt and boxer shorts, propped on the edge of his bed, handcuffed in a rear-stack position. The rear-stack, where a person's hands are secured behind their back, but one atop the other, is universally known as the safest option for cuffing potentially problematic prisoners. Liz stands in front of him.

'Morning, Jack,' she says, starting politely. There's always a chance a polite officer will encourage a polite suspect.

Jack stares at the floor. Liz nods to the constables.

One of them steps forward. 'I'm arresting you on suspicion of attempted murder, possession of a firearm, robbery and aggravated burglary. You do not have to say anything, but it may harm your defence if you do not mention now, something which you later rely on in court. Anything you do say may be given in evidence.'

Jack shakes his head, looking up at the officer through his mop of blonde hair.

'Do you understand that, Jack?' the PC asks. 'Have you got anything to say?'

'Can I get a smoke before I get in the van?'

'We'll see. Up you get, mate.'

Shaw is walked out of the house and towards the waiting prisoner van.

It's two hours later when a specialist search officer opens the loft.

'Bloody hell, it's like a fucking car boot sale exploded up here.'

'Oh dear,' says Liz, looking up at him as he stands on the loft ladder. 'You'll be a while, then?'

So far, the search of Jack Shaw's house has uncovered much of interest. The team has found multiple items of what they believe to be stolen property, as well as clothing that matches the description of what the suspects were wearing on the night of the carjacking, burglary and shooting. A small amount of cannabis has also been found, along with numerous weapons dotted around the house. Two samurai swords have been found behind doorways, a number of baseball bats placed in different rooms around the address and an axe was placed next to the front door. It's a common tactic for gang members that Liz has seen before. They need to be prepared for attacks from rival gangs at all times. But the one thing they haven't found is the shotgun.

Liz stares up at the opening to the loft and mentally crosses her fingers.

Victim 4

'Thank you so much for coming in,' Liz says to the man, as she leads him through the police station and into her office.

'No problem.'

'Did they tell you that we've got both suspects in custody now?'

'Yes, they did. Helen will be so relieved.'

Liz arrives at her desk and picks up the two exhibits that she wants to show Helen's husband.

'I can't take these out of the bags, unfortunately, but can you have a look and let me know if this is your shotgun and case?'

Helen's husband, Ian, looks closely at the items, before confirming, 'Yes, they're mine alright.'

'Thank you.' Liz beams at him. 'How is Helen doing?'

'She's been a bit of a mess since it happened, I'm afraid.'

Liz nods sympathetically. 'I'm not surprised, after what she went through.'

'I'm just so annoyed with myself that I wasn't there,' he says, rubbing a hand across his eyes. 'I'd gone to the pub for a drink – I don't go out often – I should've been at home, with Helen.'

'You can't have known.'

'She thinks they must have known she was alone.' Ian looks at Liz questioningly. 'Do you think that's true?'

'We don't know, I'm afraid. They have done this to male victims as well, we believe, so there's no reason to think that your wife was targeted specifically. We're going to try our hardest to ensure that the second suspect is also held on remand – in prison – until court. We've got some excellent evidence and witnesses, so we are hopeful of a prison sentence.'

'Good. I hope they go down for a long time. One of them had his hand over her mouth for over an hour, a machete at her neck. She can't sleep.'

'I'm so sorry.'

Liz begins to lead Ian towards the exit, her mind fast-forwarding to getting Shaw into interview. He's been in custody now for five hours, and the custody clock is tick-ing. She's only got another nineteen hours to interview him, present her case to the CPS and hopefully get permission for a charge before his custody clock runs out. She'd like to spend more time reassuring Ian, so that he in turn can reassure Helen, but she knows the best thing she can do for them both, and all the other victims in this case, is make sure Jack Shaw and Lee Benson are found guilty.

She waves him out of the front door of the police station and rushes back inside.

Suspect 2

Two hours later, Liz sits opposite Jack Shaw in an interview room. He's wearing a custody-issue grey tracksuit and is sipping at a cup of coffee, in which he demanded three sugars. A duty solicitor sits beside him.

'So, just to recap,' Liz says, tapping the notepad in front of her, 'you were seen in the location of the Astra carjack-ing just before it happened. In the recovered Astra, we found your DNA on the handbrake. I think that the suspect driving the car – the one in the photo I've shown you – is you. What do you say to that?'

'You see this photo?' Jack says, pointing to the image that Graham took of him and Lee Benson in the carjacked Astra. 'You say this is me, right?'

'I know it's you, Jack.'

'It's not me,' Jack insists, 'but if it was, like you're

saying – well, this guy is wearing gloves. So if that's me, and I'm wearing gloves, how has my DNA got on the handbrake?'

'You tell me, Jack. Maybe you got sloppy and took your gloves off? Either way we can place you in this Astra.'

'Well, I buy and sell cars, don't I? I'm in and out of a lot of cars.' Jack sits back, placing his arms behind his head, as if he's chilling out in a café having a chat with a mate.

'If it's not you in this car, where were you at the time this offence was happening?'

'No comment.'

Liz swallows her frustration at Jack's attitude. She shouldn't expect anything more from a career criminal. She reminds herself of her strategy – cover every single moment of the crime – and hears the advice of her DCI echo in her ears: *ask him where he was, who he was with, if we find an area that he's uncomfortable with, keep hammering on that nail.* Liz knows that Jack has done this dance many times before. Knows that he'll be trying to figure out what they know, and what they don't. He'll be trying to figure out an excuse for every piece of evidence she shows him.

'We've also got a balaclava, found in the Astra. It's got traces of your DNA on it.'

'No comment.'

Jack's left eye twitches.

'Is this your balaclava, Jack?'

'No comment.'

'Do you own any balaclavas?'

Jack looks to his solicitor briefly, and Liz can almost see

his brain whirring as he scrambles to think. He checks himself, remembering to appear disinterested, and leans back in his chair again, stifling a large, pretend yawn. 'Yeah, I do, actually.'

'Why do you own balaclavas?'

'I like a bit of night fishing, don't I?' He smiles at her. 'It gets cold when you're waiting for a bite.'

'And how has one of your balaclavas got in the carjacked Astra?'

'Now that you mention it, I do remember losing a couple of those things over the years. Maybe someone picked it up.'

'I think a jury will see it as proof that you committed these crimes, Jack.'

'You know, there's probably crimes happening, out there, right now. Am I getting the blame for them, too?' He laughs at his little joke, crossing his arms on the table in front of him and resting his head on them. 'I'm getting bored now, when can I go back to my cell?'

'That's the whole point of this interview, Jack – if you can tell us where you were when this was happening, then we can rule you out.'

'No comment.' His voice is muffled by his arms.

Liz decides to bring out the gun. She leans to the side and lifts it up, still encased in its secure evidential packaging, and places it heavily on the table. She's satisfied to see Jack start slightly at the noise.

'How do you explain this being found in your loft, then?'

Jack lifts his head and looks at the shotgun. 'Never seen it before in my life.'

'I find that hard to believe, Jack, since it was found hidden behind the water tank in your loft.'

'You know, I hang about with a lot of dodgy blokes. I let them stay over a hell of a lot. They've got free rein of the place – I don't ask no questions. Maybe one of them put it there.'

'Did someone ask you to hold it for them? If it's not yours, whose is it?'

'I ain't no grass, love.'

'This gun was taken from an aggravated burglary where a woman was held captive for over an hour by two suspects with machetes. You match the description of one of those men. Lee Benson matches the other.'

'No comment.'

'Guess whose DNA we found on the gun, Jack.'

He looks at her, refusing to ask.

'It's your DNA. So now we have your DNA on the hand-brake of the stolen Astra, the balaclava and the gun. It's not looking good, is it?'

'The gun was found in my house, course it's got my DNA on it. Doesn't mean I fired it.'

'Why don't you just admit your part in these crimes, Jack?'

'I wasn't part of them, no comment!'

Jack is getting annoyed. He's sitting up straight, with closed fists on the table.

Liz only has one more thing to discuss.

'Do you know what happens when you smash through a glass window or door, Jack?'

He ignores her.

'Thousands of tiny particles of glass fly out in every direction. They land everywhere. In your hair, in your clothing, all around you. We also had a number of your clothes analysed by forensic scientists. In your clothes, and in that balaclava we've been discussing, were tiny glass fragments, Jack.'

'Fuck this, I'm done – I want to go back to my cell.'

'Those glass particles have been matched to both the glass door of the house you broke into on the night of the carjacking, and the house you burglarized a week before, where you held a woman hostage and stole her husband's shotgun.'

'Fuck you.'

Fuck you too, Jack, Liz thinks as she smiles politely at him. *Fuck you.*

Lee Benson pleaded not guilty. He was found guilty at court of possession of a firearm, false imprisonment, aggravated burglary, armed robbery and taking of a car. He was sentenced to ten years in prison. Jack Shaw pleaded guilty to the offences of possession of a firearm, false imprisonment, aggravated burglary, armed robbery, taking of a car and actual bodily harm. He was sentenced to nine years in prison.

Detective Constable Elizabeth Squire spent thirty years in the Yorkshire Police Service. She progressed upwards to the rank of Detective Superintendent and spent many years in the Organized Crime Unit, contributing to the identification and disruption of criminal gangs across Yorkshire. She ended her career after over ten years of leading Murder Investigation Teams in the fight to bring killers to justice. Through her time in policing she received a number of Local, Judge's and Commissioner's commendations, and was also awarded the Long Service and Good Conduct Medal.

When asked to comment on her career in policing, she said, *'It is an incredibly privileged position to be in when the public puts their faith in you to keep them safe, and to root out those who seek to do good people harm. There are certain people who hate the police, but we continue to work to keep communities safe, to police without fear or favour, and run towards the danger when it presents itself. I'm grateful to all the wonderful colleagues I had the opportunity to work with, as every conviction gained is a team effort. I hope there are young women out there who read this book and decide to give policing a go. I would wholeheartedly recommend it as the best career ever.'*

Chapter 7

Like most UK counties, Yorkshire has a long history of sex work that dates back centuries. Back then, sex workers would gather in the dock areas as sailors, lonely from long sea voyages, disembarked their ships. Sailors proved to be eager clients, and councils and police have been trying to crack down on the problem of red-light districts in the area for the 200 years since. Many techniques used by police in the past have simply tried to move the problem elsewhere, instead of addressing the reasons that sex workers exist in the first place.

Sex workers are described as some of the women most vulnerable to rape and murder. They are also seen, by a large percentage of the public, as *imperfect victims*. They are often labelled as *sinners*, and seen as less worthy of justice than women who are deemed *innocent* victims. Although things have changed for the better in the last ten years, historically, the public has often lacked the required motivation or care to help the police investigate cases of missing sex workers. This completes the cycle of disinterest in these women, and makes them the ideal target for serial killers. The most famous of these was Peter Sutcliffe, named by the public and press as the Yorkshire Ripper. But Peter wasn't the only monster lurking amongst the county's forbidding hills and valleys.

Luckily, for the county of Yorkshire, women like Detective Chief Inspector Rosie Faulkner believe that no woman deserves to be murdered, and that every murdered woman deserves justice.

DCI Rosie Faulkner clears her throat, and the loud chatter in the briefing room dies away.

'Thank you everyone for coming. As you know, we're here today to begin conducting further land searches in the case of missing woman Amanda Hudson.' Rosie points to the large screen behind her, where Amanda's smiling face looks out over the room. 'She is twenty-seven years old and a mother to two children.'

She waits a beat, letting the idea of two children missing their mummy sink in around the assembled officers. She continues, 'Amanda was reported missing by her mother on the tenth of January 2020, which makes it over three months now that she's been gone. Up until now, this has been dealt with by the Missing Persons Unit. However, new intelligence has come to light that makes us believe Amanda could have been murdered. She has been linked to David Lewisham.' She nods to the sergeant at the computer and he clicks onto the next slide. David Lewisham's face appears on the screen.

'Some of you may have heard of him. We believe that he was responsible for the murder of Naomi Bridges in October 1995. Back then, unfortunately, a jury acquitted him. He's got multiple previous for attacking sex workers and lives within a mile of the area where Amanda disappeared. Searches have been undertaken by officers around the area for Amanda already, but in light of the fact that we now know she's been hanging around with a suspected murderer, we need to get back in there and go over everything with a fine-tooth comb.

'Before I go further into what we've got on David, I'm going to hand you over to Ryan, one of our analysts, who has put together a brief on David's life and offences up until now. This should get everyone up to speed. I want one hundred per cent focus on this, guys – engaged faces and minds, please.'

Rosie nods to Ryan, who takes her place at the front of the room whilst she sits down, to one side of the projector. She looks around the room at the cocktail of gathered staff: uniformed constables – they'll be responsible for neighbour enquiries; detectives – supervising the searches and following up on any intel the constables receive from neighbours; the two human members of a Dog Unit – their four-legged colleagues in their van outside; a specialist search team – numbering fifteen officers in all, they'll conduct a fingertip search of the area; three forensic experts; and a crime scene manager. Also present is Detective Superintendent Alan Harkwell, who is sitting to her right at the front of the room. She's glad to see alert faces and pens hovering over notebooks. Alan is fiddling with his phone next to her, but she's not about to tell a superintendent what to do.

She leans forward, listening intently as Ryan begins giving a detailed briefing on the background of their murder suspect.

'David Lewisham was born in Yorkshire on the fifth of April 1970. In 1981, when he was just eleven years old, he was sent to the children's wing of a psychiatric hospital, due to his aggressive behaviour towards others. Apparently, the facility was for "emotionally disturbed children". He was described by a staff member as being polite one minute, then flying into violent rages the next, targeting the other children in the facility. After his release, he attacked his sister with a bat. When he was fourteen, he allegedly tried to cut the neck of a fellow school pupil, with some scissors he'd stolen. At eighteen, he tried to stab a young relative in the neck.

'He joined the Navy at eighteen, but was reprimanded for theft and criminal damage after he got angry about his favourite soap on the telly. He apparently didn't like the way the story was going and smashed up the television with a chair.'

A chuckle of disbelief around the room, and Ryan pauses, gulping from a bottle of water. Rosie writes *short fuse* on her notepad and circles it.

'He continued to display threatening behaviour through-out his twenties, including threatening a neighbour with a knife, and breaking someone's fingers after a disagreement. Moving forward to when he's twenty-seven . . .' The analyst pauses as he shuffles through his papers. 'Ah, here we are – April 1995, three schoolgirls found the body of a sex worker, 25-year-old Naomi Bridges, in an overgrown wasteland ditch they stumbled into whilst playing.'

Rosie winces. Why do these women's names always have to be prefixed with the sins the public believe them to have committed? She resists the urge to call him out in front of everyone, no need to embarrass him. A quiet chat after the briefing should suffice.

'The victim had been stamped on, and her body had multiple – horrific, according to the pathologist – injuries. Death was found to be due to a large gash wound to her neck. There was a lack of leads at the time, probably because she was a sex worker, the public didn't seem that interested. The police at the time tried public appeals and even *Crimewatch*, but got nothing significant. It was only when Lewisham was arrested for drink-driving, in September 1995, that he was linked to Naomi's murder via his DNA. He stood trial in early 2000, but as we know, he was acquitted. His story was that he paid Naomi for sex, but he "didn't enjoy it", causing them to argue. She then left the car and that was the last time he saw her. We

release by drinking and removing his tag, which resulted in him being recalled to prison later on in 2003 and again in 2004. He got extra time for the breaches, ending up in him serving ten years, and he was released in 2010. Once he got out, he moved back to Yorkshire, and police here were still convinced that he'd killed Naomi Bridges and that he was a massive threat to women, especially sex workers. They began Operation Motel, which was a year-long under-cover op involving multiple officers. They got hundreds of hours of undercover recordings, including a confession to the actual murder. They had to stop the op when Lewisham *again* attacked a prostitute – sorry, sex worker – and·was sent back to prison in 2011 for breaching the conditions of his Sexual Offences Prevention Order.

'By this time, double-jeopardy laws had been changed and this meant that there was a possibility Lewisham could be tried again for Naomi's murder. Yorkshire Police and the CPS took the confession to the Court of Appeal, but they denied the appeal, saying that the new evidence wasn't "compelling" enough.'

'How is a confession not compelling enough?' a PC from the back asks.

Ryan shrugs. 'Don't ask me.' He turns to Rosie. 'That's pretty much all I've got, guv.'

Rosie stands. 'Thank you, Ryan, very comprehensive.' She takes her place at the head of the briefing once again. 'As I said before, initially a missing persons case – the miss-ing persons team at the time got multiple witness reports of sightings of Amanda after she disappeared, but many of these were unconfirmed, and seem to have muddied the water somewhat. They were also looking at the possibility that she had taken her own life, as her mother reported that she was trying to get off drugs and out of sex work, but had many "demons" that kept her stuck in the game. It was considered that she may have returned to Ireland, where her family lived for over ten years when she was younger, or that she had become involved in sex trafficking.

'The last CCTV we have of her is in the town centre on the thirty-first of December. There's quite a lot of footage before that showing her in the company of various men, in sex-work hotspots, so we know she was working. We found out that she was an acquaintance of David's yesterday, and he was arrested last night – apologies again to those of you who were up late and back in early this morning.' A few weary nods from around the room.

'David is still on licence, and this includes the order that he is not to associate with sex workers, or be in areas where they are known to operate. We used this to get him nicked for breach of licence, and get in there and search his address. We found a number of items which have increased our suspicions further that he may have seriously hurt or killed Amanda. Firstly, an old model mobile phone was found with multiple images of dead and mutilated women.'

Silence around the room. She pauses, the images flashing before her eyes, and takes a sip of water to cover her emotion.

'We also found images of Amanda on his phone, apparently alive and well, but in various stages of undress. In addition, there are recordings of him shouting at a woman, believed to be Amanda. With his history, it's highly likely that he's killed her, and we are sadly looking for a body today. There's been absolutely no proof of life since she went missing; she's not used her phone, she's not picked up her benefits, nothing.

'As Lewisham dumped Naomi's body in scrubland, we're going to focus on any overgrown, neglected scrub areas – Danny, the search coordinator, will take you through the areas of note.'

Rosie hands over to Danny, who displays a large map of the area on the projector screen. As he details the landscape to the team, Rosie flicks through her briefing pack until she reaches the photograph of Naomi's body. Lewisham's first victim. Pale skin. Injuries red, blue and black. Face down in the ditch. Discarded like nothing more than a sex doll he was finished with. Sadness threatens to overwhelm her as bile rises in her throat. She swallows it down. She's never been good with dead bodies, but it's not something she's going to admit to her colleagues. Imagine – a squeamish DCI, in charge of a murder squad. She returns her attention to the briefing, losing herself in the abandoned green spaces of Yorkshire.

It's two hours into the search, and Rosie is sitting in her office, slogging through paperwork, when the phone rings. It's one of her detective sergeants.

'We've found her.'

*

DCI Rosie Faulkner stands on the edge of what may once have been a stream, but is now a dusty ditch. It runs along the back of a housing estate, in a belt of green land around thirty metres wide. She doesn't know who owns the land but whoever it is has left it to grow wild. The ditch is barely visible, overgrown weeds and bushes so thick along its borders that you'd never even know it was there. Luckily, Rosie has the cadaver dogs on her team, and they'd tracked directly to this spot.

Amanda's body lies before her, face down in the dried mud. She is partially dressed; the clothes remaining are dirty, bloodstained and torn. She had been covered by stones and gravel, which the forensic team have now cleared away. Rosie looks at the small hand nearest her, splayed open, wrist rotated so that her palm is to the sky. She wants to hold it. Instead, she clears her throat, to get the attention of the pathologist.

'It fits our suspect's MO of dumping in ditches.'

'At least it's dry mud,' the pathologist says, smiling. 'Better for us.'

'Can you give me anything?'

'Not much yet. Body looks to have been here a good while, decomposition is advanced, which makes it difficult to see how she was killed. I won't know till she's on the table.'

Rosie nods. A constable is hurrying towards them, carrying a large tent bag on his shoulder.

'Get that up, asap,' Rosie commands. 'It won't be long till the vultures descend.'

*

DCI Faulkner takes a seat at the long briefing table. She looks out into a packed room of reporters. There's an assortment of phones and press cameras being held in the air, and the room is filled with the loud murmurs of the media. To her left are Amanda's husband, Darren, and mother. The words of her superior, Detective Superintendent Alan Harkwell, are still ringing in her ears – *we're being criticized for not finding the body first time round* – as she stands and claps her hands, bringing the room to silence.

'Thank you all for coming. We'll be making some pre-prepared statements. Amanda's family will speak after me and won't be taking any questions. I'd like you all to respect that, please.'

She sits back down and nods to the cameras. Her heart is beating so loud that she is convinced the multiple microphones on the table in front of her must be picking up the sound of it. She hates these things, but they are necessary. She takes a breath and begins.

'We can now confirm that the female body found yesterday in the scrubland to the rear of Redbrick Estate was that of Amanda Hudson, who was last seen on New Year's Eve, the thirty-first of December 2019. This is now a murder investigation. A man has been taken into custody in relation to Amanda's killing. However, we still need the public's help in gathering any sightings or evidence of Amanda's movements since she went missing.

'I do want to firstly reiterate that this has been an extremely complex investigation with many unconfirmed sightings reported in the initial weeks of Amanda's disappearance. For this reason, the case was treated as a missing persons investigation until recently. We discovered Amanda's body during a second search of extremely overgrown and partially inaccessible scrubland; this second search was more thorough, as at this point, we were sadly looking for remains. Officers have been working extremely hard to find Amanda since she was reported missing.

'I do believe that the answers to what happened to Amanda can be found within our local community and I encourage people to please come forward and speak to us. We are looking for these specific items, believed to have been worn by Amanda on the night she was killed.' Rosie glances to the screen behind her, where similar items of clothing to the ones Amanda was wearing when she went missing are being displayed. 'I do believe that these items could have been discarded in the local area. Someone could have found them – if you have, please get in touch. No information is too small to help with this case. Please contact us if you knew Amanda or if you believe you saw her at any point before or after she went missing.

'We believe that she may have built up some kind of relationship with a local man and are particularly interested in any information you may have about her friendships, who she may have been associating with and places she regularly went, or people she regularly spent time with.'

Rosie looks to Darren, who nods at her.

'Amanda's family will now make a statement.'

'Amanda moved with her family to this area for a better life.' His voice is wobbly, but he lifts his chin and continues, looking as if it is taking all of his strength to do so. 'She was a much-loved wife, daughter, sister and mother to two children. She believed that her children would have a better life here. Sadly, she separated from us all, her family, which led her life to become more transient and chaotic. Although her life took a dark path, she was still a mother, and she will be greatly missed by her children, and all of us. Please, if you have any information about what happened to her, please give it to the police. Thank you.'

A reporter calls out from the front row. Rosie recognizes him from previous press conferences and grits her teeth.

'How do you feel about your wife becoming a sex worker?'

Darren's face pales, and the officers around him – the family liaison officers who have been supporting the family since Amanda disappeared – immediately usher him and Amanda's mother from the room. Rosie stares at the reporter until he looks away. It's intrusive reporters like him that write salacious articles about the killing of women, revelling in highlighting a woman's profession if she is a sex worker. It's tabloids like the one he works for that perpetuate damaging attitudes to sex workers, and sometimes dissuade the public from coming forward.

Rosie steps into the warm fug of a busy, old-fashioned café, just outside town. She's been told to head to the back, and she walks between the tables and chairs until she reaches an archway that reveals a small area to the right, invisible from the street. There are two tables in this area; one is empty, and at the other sits a skinny bald man covered in tattoos. He waves, and she approaches the table.

'Mike?' she asks, though she knows he's not actually called Mike.

'Sit down, love.' He nods to the seat in front of him. 'You eating?'

Her stomach rumbles in reply. 'No.'

'Straight down to it.' He wipes a paper napkin across his mouth and pushes the empty plate in front of him to one side. 'I'll start at the beginning – do stop me if you have any questions.'

'Thanks, great.' Rosie smiles. She places her phone on the table in front of her and says, 'Do you mind if I record this? Just for my own notes.'

'I'd rather you didn't.' The man sits back in his chair and folds his arms. He's a member of the undercover team that befriended David Lewisham for almost a year. She'd heard that undercover officers were cagey. To get this meeting, she'd had to jump through various size hoops and grease a number of wheels. But she needed to know who Lewisham was, and who better to tell her than a man who'd been close to him for almost a year.

'No worries,' she says, not wanting to put him off, and pockets her mobile, pulling out her notebook and pen instead. She scribbles the date at the top and looks to Mike.

'It was a long year, with David. Took a while to gain his trust in the beginning. There was a group of us, and we all played a different role. Members of a criminal gang. It was pretty good the way it came together. My backstory was that I was a criminal who'd got into some trouble with a drugs gang in Scotland. There was a price on my head and I had to take them out before they did me in.

'I approached him in his local and asked if he wanted to make a quick bit of money. At first, we just set up fake deliveries and pick-ups for him to do for me. Kept him busy, gave him cash here and there. Then I asked for his help to scare someone that owed me money. We drove to a block of garages, and one of the other officers was there, pretending to fix a car. I told Lewisham to back me up, stand behind me and say nothing. I got out of the car and grabbed the other officer, started punching him in the face.'

Rosie must have looked surprised, because Mike pauses, and says, 'I know. It's fucking full on. We're mates, this officer and me, and I basically had to give him a couple of black eyes.

'Anyway, he acts scared and gives the impression that I'm someone not to be messed with. It's all about adding layers of the story, making it seem believable, so that Lewisham would be completely convinced that we were legit. Bloke was a fucking coward.' He laughs, then takes a gulp of his tea. 'I turned round once my mate was on the floor and Lewisham's cowering in the car. He tried to make out that he thought he heard my mobile ringing, but it was in my pocket. He was shitting bricks. All the things he talks about doing to women, you put a man in front of him and he'd piss his pants.' Mike shakes his head in disgust.

'So, he would talk about women, sex workers?' Rosie asks.

'Oh yeah. Don't think I ever heard him actually use the word woman, though. It was always bitches, sluts, dogs. One of our team was a female officer, pretending to be a sex worker that "serviced" the gang. We didn't want Lewisham getting any ideas, so he was told she was off limits. But she introduced the discussion of prossies.'

Rosie raises an eyebrow.

'Sorry.' He shrugs. 'When I start talking about this stuff I automatically get sucked back into the role. The lingo. Anyway, Jane – that was her undercover name – she was there to get him talking about women. His eyes were all over her, all of the time. It was embarrassing, almost, like he was a fucking teenager who couldn't control himself. Every day I wanted to kick the living shit out of him.'

Rosie nods. 'I can understand why.'

'Another thing we did, we got some clothing and soaked it in pig's blood. A butcher I know sorted us out. Lovely steaks, he does. So, we get these blood-soaked clothes and I call Lewisham telling him I need his help urgently. I give him the clothes and tell him to burn them. He's got a burner phone at this point that we've given him, and he videos himself burning the clothes, sending me the video as proof that he'd done it. I knew at that point that he was in deep. He one hundred per cent believed that we were crooks.'

'The level of effort you guys put into this is impressive.'

'It's all theatre.' Mike makes a jazz-hands gesture, and Rosie chuckles. 'Although, I have to say, it's rare to go that dark.'

'I've never heard of such tactics!'

'That's kind of the point.' Mike continues the story. 'So, he's in deep. We know that he trusts us. We're drinking one night and I say that I need someone killed. That I need his help. He says it won't be a problem as he's killed someone before. You should've felt my pulse when he said that. But he'd been drinking, hadn't he? A drunk confession wouldn't cut it in court, so I had to stop him.'

'Shit,' Rosie exclaims.

'Yeah. So,' Mike lifts a finger, 'a few days later, I circle back to needing him for this job. Give him a hard time for hiding in the car before, y'know, tell him that I'm not sure I can depend on him. I thought he would confess again, he was so desperate to please, but he just says that violence isn't a problem for him. I thought we'd blown it.' Mike shakes his head, takes another large gulp from his tea. 'About a month later, sober, he just comes out with it. Jane and I had just had a fake row, I basically treated her like shit in front of Lewisham. I wanted him to think we were the same.'

Mike drags a hand across his mouth and chin. 'I've got a wife. Two daughters. Some of the things he said about women.' He shakes his head. 'He is a sick, sick puppy. All of the shit I had to say to make him think I was anywhere near like him – I still think about it now – but I knew that he was too dangerous to be on the streets. Knew we had to get him locked up. So, it was worth it, you know?'

He wants her to understand. She nods.

'Anyway, Jane leaves in a huff after our "row" and

Lewisham starts asking me why I put up with her. He goes off on this rant about sex workers, how they're scum, that I shouldn't put up with her shit. I'm listening to him rave on, and he just says it. Just lays it out for me.'

'What did he say?' Rosie is leaning forward now, hands flat on the table.

'He told me he used to know a whore like that, his words, and that she was doing his nut in, so he killed her and dumped her in a ditch. It took all of my training not to knock him out right there, I tell you. The way he talked about her – Naomi – like she was a broken telly he'd fly-tipped.'

'All on tape?'

'Clear as a bell.'

'How on earth wasn't that enough to try him again for Naomi's murder?'

'The double-jeopardy stuff was all new. The only case that had been tried again since the law change was based on new forensic findings. I think, at that time, that the Court of Appeal wanted forensics, they needed something solid, to agree to retry. It was incredibly frustrating – and that's me being polite. Of course, afterwards, Lewisham insisted that he'd made everything up, that he was only trying to impress me.'

'I can only imagine how annoyed you all were, after all that time and effort. And you had to stop because he attacked another sex worker?'

'Yeah.' He's finished his tea and begins to fidget, glancing at his watch. 'Have you got what you needed?'

Rosie nods. 'Yes, thanks very much, this has been invaluable.'

'I hope you get the bastard.' Mike stands. 'He needs putting away. For ever.'

Rosie waits in the custody suite of a Yorkshire police station. Footsteps approach from her right, and she turns to see two detention officers leading David Lewisham from the direction of the cells, towards her. She's watched his interview tapes, but this is the first time she has come face to face with the man. She was expecting a monster and berates herself for once again giving purchase in her mind to the make-believe world of good and evil. Monsters don't exist. Just fucked-up people.

Lewisham walks towards the custody desk and faces the sergeant who is standing on the other side. Lewisham turns his head and looks at Rosie, a smile playing on his lips.

'Who's this, then?' he asks. 'I've not seen you before.'

'I'm DCI Faulkner, and I'll be charging you today.'

The smile drops from Lewisham's face and he lowers his gaze to Rosie's chest, where it lingers. 'Well, at least I've got a good view.' He smirks.

One of the detention officers moves to step between Lewisham and Rosie, but Rosie raises a hand. She can deal with creeps. She turns to the custody sergeant and begins to read out the charges. Lewisham says nothing, and she can feel his eyes boring into her the whole time. She reads slowly and clearly, refusing to let his lecherous stare unnerve her. Once she has finished, the custody sergeant instructs the detention officers to escort Lewisham back to his cell.

He takes one last look at Rosie over his shoulder as they lead him away.

She shivers. Maybe evil does exist, after all.

Rosie rushes up the stairs, to the second floor of the CPS building. Inside, a highly experienced lawyer waits to discuss their strategy.

'Sorry, hope you've not been waiting long.' She hurries to the table and sits down, trying to swallow the heavy breathing brought on by the stairs.

The woman introduces herself. Her name is familiar, and Rosie smiles. 'Anna, I think we've been exchanging emails for the last few months? Nice to finally put a face to the name.'

'Likewise.' Anna returns the smile.

There's a plate of sad-looking biscuits in the centre of the table, and Anna asks Rosie if she'd like a drink.

'Oh, no, thank you.' Rosie waves a hand. 'I stopped at Costa earlier so I'm all caffeinated.'

'Excellent,' Anna says. 'Let's get started, then.'

'I had the pleasure of reading Lewisham his charges a couple of weeks ago – there's something extremely wrong with this man. We need to get him off the streets, and keep him off them.'

Anna nods, and Rosie knows that they're on the same page. That Anna is the kind of woman who gets it, when you tell her to avoid a dodgy colleague, or not to be in the same room as a certain man. 'Take me through the evidence you have so far, in relation to Amanda's murder.'

'Right,' Rosie begins, 'we've got multiple witnesses who confirm that Amanda and Lewisham had been associating with each other for at least a couple of months before she went missing. Luckily, his close neighbours have CCTV, and this shows Amanda coming and going from the address in the run-up to New Year's Eve. We seized a phone that has a recording on it, believed to be of Lewisham and Amanda – her husband has listened to the tape and given us a statement to say that he believes it's Amanda's voice – in it, Lewisham is shouting at her. He says . . .' Rosie pauses, scanning her notes. 'Here it is: *if you come back here, I will hurt you. I will hurt you so bad you'll not be able to walk for months*. So there's your evidence that he means to do her serious harm. After that threat was recorded, she was seen again on CCTV, in and out of some of the pubs in town, before the last sighting of her, where she is seen walking alone towards the road that leads to Lewisham's flat. Our theory is that she returns to his flat and he carries out an attack on her, killing her.'

'She obviously didn't realize just how dangerous he was,' says Anna sadly.

'Exactly,' Rosie agrees. 'We don't have direct evidence that she returned there, but considering he threatened to kill her if she did, and now she's dead, hopefully a jury will agree that it's most likely that she did. Our theory is that he killed her either New Year's Eve or early hours of New Year's Day. On the second of January, we've got him purchasing a bundle of towels, a shovel, a huge pack of wet wipes and some rubber gloves at nearby shops. It's disturbing how relaxed he looks on the CCTV.'

'What else have we got?'

'There're the searches we found on his laptop and phone. He was viewing a lot of violent porn, obviously, but apparently that's normal now.' She shrugs at Anna, who rolls her eyes. 'He made searches on *how to commit the perfect murder* and *how to dispose of a body so it will never be found.* These searches go back to before he even met Amanda, which makes me think that he actually targeted her. Her family has said that she was at a really low point in her life. She was relying heavily on drugs, was totally isolated from her friends and family. Other witnesses say that Lewisham was paying her for sex. It's like he's drawn her in, pretending to help her, giving her money so she could keep using. I think he knew that he wanted to kill again, and he chose to get to know her for this reason. He also had hundreds of images of dead women, or women posed to look dead, on his phone. All downloaded from the internet.'

'He was obsessed with the idea of killing another woman.' Anna shakes her head. 'That's what we need to convince the jury of.'

'We've also got statements from some of Lewisham's probation officers. Some of the things he's said to them are absolutely shocking; how he wasn't recalled to prison, when he was clearly a danger to women, is beyond me.' Rosie again looks to her notes. 'One of the probation officers says that Lewisham has shown a strong dislike for sex workers, has described them as *easy targets, scum – the lowest of the low –* he's also apparently said, and this is a direct quote, *I just want to hurt people.*'

'Jesus,' Anna mutters, scribbling furiously.

'Another officer said that he described enjoying the *pleasure of hurting*, and that he liked to watch women panic. Apparently, when she asked him what he wants to do to women, he said *you know I can't tell you what I want to do to them.*'

Anna is silent, seemingly lost in thought. Rosie tries not to think about what Amanda's last moments must have been like. After a few seconds, Anna gives herself a tiny shake and asks, 'What defence has he given in interviews?'

'Absolutely nothing,' Rosie answers. 'He's gone *no comment* for every single one.'

'Frustrating,' Anna says, 'but we have to assume that his defence is going to be similar to the one he used back in 2000 when he denied Naomi's murder. That he paid her for sex, and she was absolutely fine the last time he saw her.'

'Will we be able to try him for Naomi's murder too? What's the situation with the double-jeopardy law?'

'We've sent the request to the Court of Appeal. Hopefully, this new murder case will qualify as compelling enough for them to agree to a retrial. If we can try him for Naomi's 1995 murder at the same time as Amanda's, we'll have a much stronger case. We're also hoping to be able to use the intelligence gleaned during Op Motel, including his confession. That, added to his previous convictions of attacks against sex workers should help us too.'

'Will his previous convictions be allowed?' Rosie asks.

'We hope so. We're certainly going to give it our best shot at getting them in. The fact that he was attacking more sex workers just weeks after being acquitted of Naomi's murder in 2000 is compelling.'

'I just hope the jury sees it that way.'

'We can but hope,' Anna says.

Rosie thinks, not for the first time, that juries should be abolished. It may have been a good idea, hundreds of years ago, for a person to be tried by a jury of their peers. For average members of the public to make decisions on life and death. But right now, the more she deals with average members of the public, the more she thinks the majority of them are total imbeciles.

David Lewisham stands in the dock.

Rosie sits in the gallery, one hand on top of the other in her lap. Two of the fingers of her lower hand are crossed so tight that they're beginning to ache. She had been confident throughout the trial. All of the evidence that the CPS had wanted to include had been allowed – Lewisham's previous convictions, his assaults on sex workers, his disturbing comments to his probation officers and his taped confession. It seems impossible that the jury would find him anything other than guilty. But the prosecution goes first, followed by the defence. Lewisham's defence was the last thing that the jurors heard before they left to make their verdict. His excuses fresh in their mind. Their own prejudices about sex workers already with them, ingrained no doubt for years.

Lewisham has admitted to knowing Amanda. Has admitted to her being at his house and to paying her for sex. There were no forensics from either woman's body that categorically pointed towards him being the killer. He came across as calm and reasonable in the witness box. He stuck to his story, despite intensive questioning from the CPS barrister, that Amanda had left his flat on the evening of New Year's Eve and had not returned. She wouldn't trust him as far as she could throw him, she still remembered the way he had looked at her when she'd read him the murder charges. She can only hope that the jury can see through his Mr Nice Guy act.

In previous cases, she's been convinced that someone will be found guilty, only for the jury to disagree. She looks to Amanda's husband, surrounded by his family, and then, two rows back, to Naomi's mother. Pain etched in every line of her weathered face.

'Have you reached a verdict upon which you are all agreed?'

Rosie snaps back to attention as the clerk stands and addresses the jury foreperson, who is also standing. The jury was out for five hours. Not long to decide the fate of a man's life. She's learnt never to try to predict what the verdict will be by the amount of time it took to reach. Quick can be a good sign. It can also be bad.

'Yes, we have,' says the foreperson.

'On the charge of the murder of Amanda Hudson on or around the thirty-first of December 2019, how do you find the defendant?'

The whole court is still and the moment stretches outwards in all directions, sweat gathering between Rosie's fingers.

'Guilty.'

A cheer erupts from the public gallery. Rosie's heart soars, but she doesn't react – not just yet – not until she's got justice for both women.

'On the charge of the murder of Naomi Bridges in the month of October 1995, how do you find the defendant?'

'Guilty.' The foreperson's voice rings out across the courtroom, prompting another cheer from the gallery.

Lewisham remains completely impassive, his face blank, as gasps and claps ring out from the gallery above him. Rosie's face breaks into a wide smile and she looks upwards towards Naomi's and Amanda's families. Justice at last.

In the judge's summing-up of the murder cases, he told Lewisham that he had committed the most brutal, callous murders of two women, and accused him of choosing them because they were sex workers, whom Lewisham had thought had no value. The judge hoped that the public could now see that sex workers have just as much value as anyone else, and apologized for the lack of initial justice served to Naomi's family, and for the extended length of time that they had to wait for it.

David Lewisham was ordered to serve a minimum term of thirty-seven years in prison. He will not be eligible for parole until 2058, at which point he will be eighty-eight years old.

DCI Rosie Faulkner spent thirty-one years policing in various areas of Yorkshire. During her career, she rose to the rank of Detective Superintendent and was in charge of many murder investigations. She was the recipient of a Police Long Service and Good Conduct Medal and multiple awards and commendations. Her service was described as exemplary.

Chapter 8

The public can sometimes forget that police officers are real people, with real lives, families and friends. Who they were before they joined the police follows them into their careers, where things like previous relationships, complicated personal stories and a shady past, can all come back to haunt officers of the law. It is often tricky policing in the same area as where you grew up. Long-term loyalties, or grievances, can make impartial policing a difficult task. Our fictional sergeant, Catherine, has a backstory full of the twists and turns of a difficult life. She is devastated when she learns that her sister, Clare, has betrayed her by helping Ryan visit his psychotic father, Tommy Lee Royce, in prison.

Clare and Catherine's relationship has not always been

a smooth one. Clare is a recovering addict, and we see throughout *Happy Valley* that Catherine can't always be sure that Clare isn't hiding things from her. One area, however, where Catherine is sure they agree, is that Ryan must be protected from Tommy Lee Royce, at all costs. When Clare risks Ryan's safety, it threatens to destroy their relationship for good.

Whilst Catherine's and Clare's stories are fictitious, many real-life police officers patrol the streets they grew up in, especially in predominantly rural counties like Yorkshire. What do you do, as a police officer, if your best friend grows up on the other side of the law? When Sergeant Claire Lesley was faced with a choice between her best friend and the law, it was the most difficult decision of her life.

Thirteen years old

Sergeant Claire Lesley grew up in Yorkshire, among the community she now polices. Being a *born-local* copper brings its advantages and disadvantages. The fact that she recognizes some of the youths in front of her, and knows where to find their mothers, is an advantage. The fact that one of them is her best friend's daughter, Lacey, is definitely not.

She's been called to the Homefield estate after residents reported a group of kids smashing windows. The informant told police that the kids were all aged around sixteen.

Lacey is thirteen. She's tall and watches YouTube make-up videos, covering her perfect skin with imperfect products that make her look older. There're seven kids in all, five girls and two boys, all clad in designer knock-offs. The girls' faces are plastered similarly to Lacey's, each one trying to look just like the others. Claire thinks back to the make-up from her youth – a swipe of blue eyeshadow, some awful-coloured lipstick, and you were done. One of the boys is older than the rest, a faint outline of a future moustache on his top lip. He has his arm slung proprietarily over Lacey's shoulder.

Lacey's eyes go wide as Claire approaches, but the rest of the group casually side-eye her, or show no sign that they've noticed her at all. Claire resists the urge to slap Bumfluff's arm off her goddaughter.

'You lot,' Claire growls. 'Apparently, there's been some windows smashed. Wouldn't 'appen to know anything about that, would you?'

The group shake their heads and Claire is reminded of a pack of sloths, their heads slowly moving in unison, to the same unbothered beat. All except Lacey, who has her eyes on the ground. Before she approached the group, Claire had looked for broken windows. She hadn't found any. Sometimes people embellish the facts in order to get the police to turn up. There are a lot of elderly residents in this part of the estate, and it doesn't take much to intimidate them.

'Do any of you live on this estate?'

Another round of slow shakes.

'Right then – you've no reason to be here.'

Bumfluff speaks up, his voice surprisingly deep. 'It's a free country.'

Claire snorts. 'Who told you that?'

'My pa says we pay your wages.' He smirks. 'Don't that make me your boss?'

A smattering of giggles from the group.

'I've heard that one before,' Claire says, stepping closer to him, a waft of stale fags and Lynx assaulting her nostrils. 'Problem is, you need a job to pay taxes. Has he got a job? How about you?'

His eyes shift away from hers and he shrugs, a faint redness blooming on his cheeks as the giggles die away.

'You know how long I've lived round 'ere?' She addresses all of them now. 'My whole life. I went to school with your mothers' – a pointed look at Lacey – 'so what I'm going to do is give you the chance to clear off home, before I start taking names and putting hands in pockets.'

The group quickly begin to disperse, and as Bumfluff turns to leave, Claire places a hand on his shoulder.

'Not you.'

Now that she's spent an unfortunate amount of time looking at his face, she can see that he is older than she first thought. The shadow on his lip is stubble. She looks to Lacey, who is walking in the direction of her flat. Now that she's away from the group, she looks like a small girl again, that awkward stage between childhood and womanhood making her arms and legs gangly.

Claire turns her attention back to Bumfluff.

'How old are you?'

He sticks out his chin. 'Fifteen.'

'That girl you had your arm round. She's thirteen.'

He shrugs. Claire grits her teeth, imagining backhanding him right across his pathetic little moustache.

'You like little girls?'

'No,' he mutters into the ground, a crack in his voice.

'You know what they do to nonces round here?' Claire's voice is low. 'We wouldn't want it getting round that you like hanging about with children, would we?'

'I'm not – I don't!'

'What's your name?'

'I don't need to tell you that.'

'Another thing your pa taught you?' Claire snorts again. 'He sounds nice.'

'I ain't done nothing wrong.'

'Arms out,' Claire says, stepping back so that she can watch his hands. She's losing patience, but reminds herself that he may be right. He hasn't done anything wrong – yet. She realizes she doesn't care. 'I'm detaining you for the purpose of a search.'

'What? What for?' Despite his protestations, he raises his arms.

Claire runs her hands along his arms, up and into each armpit and across his torso. 'Well, you're being evasive, you're hanging about with children much younger than you, and I think I can smell cannabis.'

'That's bollocks! I ain't even had a joint yet.'

'Well,' she puffs, bending to run her hands up and down his legs, being careful to use the back of her hands when near his crotch, 'you've just admitted you're a habitual drug user.'

'This is a fucking joke.'

Claire pulls a thick wallet out of his jeans pocket. Inside is an apprentice ID card, with a photo. She holds it up. 'James Brice, sixteen *next month*.' She waves the ID in his face.

'Yeah, so?' He tries for bravado but still comes off scared.

'So – now I know who you are.'

He gulps, and she slides his ID back into his wallet and hands it back to him. Satisfied that he has nothing of note on him, she steps back and folds her arms.

'James.' She smiles and looks him right in the eye. 'If I see you with Lacey again, I won't be so friendly. In fact, if I *ever* see you hanging about with young girls again, I'll make sure that everyone knows about it.'

He opens his mouth to protest, but thinks better of it, his scrawny Adam's apple wobbling impotently.

'Do you understand me, James?'

'Yeah.'

She flicks her chin at him, indicating that he may leave, and she watches him scurry away, hoping that she's put the fear of God into him.

Later that evening, Claire calls Lacey's mum, June. The dial tone sounds for a long time, and Claire is about to give up when June answers.

''Lo?'

'June?'

'Hey, love.' She sounds as if she's just woken up.

'Did Lacey get in okay?'

'Lacey?' June's voice is slurred, and Claire's heart sinks.

'Yeah, I ran into her earlier, hanging round outside the tower blocks.'

'Oh right.' The sound of a hand covering the receiver and a muffled June shouting for Lacey. 'Yeah, she's upstairs. All fine.'

'She was with some older lads, June, not a good sort.'

'Oh right.' A slight pause and a yawn. 'I'll talk to her.'

'How are you? Sorry I've not been round . . . work – y'know.' Claire looks to her lap, knowing that they both know work isn't the real reason.

Claire had grown up living next door to June. On the Yorkshire estate, they were pressed together until they were as close as their terraced houses were. Always together – they constantly tried to fool any new kids to the area that they were sisters. It was the early eighties and both their fathers lost their jobs due to the mining strikes. Claire's father turned to any old odd job to bring in a bit of cash, and June's father turned to drink. As June talks, telling Claire that things are fine, that she's been looking for a job, that she's given up the fags – well, almost – and that Lacey seems happy at school, Claire thinks back to the days when she would sneak open the back door for June. The days when the shared wall of Claire's house would almost shake from the shouting next door, and June would scurry in, straight to the TV room, where they'd ask Claire's mum to turn up whatever she was watching and cuddle under a blanket together.

'How are your AA meetings going?' Claire interrupts June's feeble attempt at happy chatter.

A pause. They never lie to each other. Claire could tell she was off the wagon the second June picked up the phone.

'You can get back on – June, you have to. Remember what social services said.'

'Yeah.' June's voice is so sad that Claire squeezes her eyes shut, cursing herself for not being there enough. 'I'm coming over tomorrow morning, I'm off shift. There's a ten a.m. meeting at the church round corner, isn't there?'

'You know the timetable better than me,' June says, a note of humour in her voice.

Claire looks at the clock; it's just before 9.30 p.m. 'Why don't you get your head down now, get a good night's sleep. You can start again tomorrow. One day at a time. I'll – I'll be around more.' Even as she says it, she doubts herself.

Fourteen

It's 2 a.m. and Claire is on a night duty. It's a Tuesday. The pub fights of the weekend aren't usually a problem mid-week and the late-night domestics have mostly finished. With a rare bit of free time, Claire has parked up on the main road out of town, lights off, settled back in her seat with one eye open for drunk drivers. The older she gets, the harder she finds it to stay awake on a night shift. It's okay if you're busy. God knows there's a ton of paperwork she could be keeping busy with back at the nick, but her eyes needed a break from the fluorescent strip lights of the office. She wanted to get out and about, remind herself what the job was like before she became responsible for a whole team of PCs and their respective fuck-ups.

What she'd really like to do is take a drunk driver off the streets. She's aware of the conversations that happen in pubs across her patch because she's heard them. *Coppers are never out on the country roads, you'll be fine, have another.* People drive themselves to the pub with the intention of getting a taxi home. Maybe it's even an honest intention. But when they're kicked out at eleven to face the biting northern winds and it's a choice between their warm car and a bitter wait for an expensive taxi, their resolve tends to waver. Then there's those who just don't care. They've done it all their lives and why should they stop now? There're the ones who are overconfident in their driving skills, generally men, convinced that they're still safe to drive after five pints with their mates because of their self-awarded prowess on the roads. It doesn't matter the reason. People who drink and drive risk lives every time they choose to get behind the wheel. They routinely take mothers away from children, husbands away from wives, and babies away from parents.

She imagines taking convicted drink drivers out on a shift. Better yet, sitting them in a traffic-patrol car. She thinks the courts should keep the driving ban, but change the fine to what she'd call a 'crash awareness course'. Send them to the wrecks like the ones they could have caused. Make them look into the dead eyes of mothers, fathers and children. Tiny babies in car seats, impossibly still. Ban them from driving for two years for a first offence and show them the realities of drinking and driving. Ban them for life on their second offence. Anyone who can see what she's seen and still take a drink before climbing into their car should never get behind the wheel.

She's interrupted from single-handedly rebuilding the justice system in her mind by her mobile phone buzzing in her pocket. She pulls it out and holds it up, frowning at the display, before picking up.

'Auntie Claire?'

'Lacey?' Claire's heart pounds at the sound of the girl's voice, small and shaky.

'Can you come get me?'

'Aren't you at home? Where's your mum?' She's sitting up straight now, phone pressed to her ear.

'I snuck out – please – I need you.' Claire can hear traffic in the background of the call and her mind races at the thought of Lacey being out so late. She twists the key in the ignition.

'Where are you?'

Claire flicks on the blue lights and throws her car into a tight U-turn. As she begins to drive to Lacey's location, she justifies her actions in her mind. She's on duty. She's driving a job car for a personal errand, and she's driving it fast. Every use of the emergency lights and sirens, every *blue-light run*, needs to be justified. If she can't justify it, and she has an accident, or worse, hits someone, then she could lose everything. Her police licence. Her job. Her freedom.

She shakes her head at the ridiculousness of her thought process. A girl is in trouble – *there's all the justification you need*. She doesn't care that it's personal. She needs to get to Lacey. She pushes her foot down on the accelerator and grips the wheel.

It has started to rain in the seven minutes it's taken Claire to get from one end of the town to the other. She slows as she turns onto the road Lacey gave her, flicking on her side spotlights and cruising slowly, eyes on the pavements either side. *Where is she?* She curses herself for not forcing Lacey to stay on the line, or asking what she was wearing. *What if you can't find her? What if she's not here? What if someone's taken her and you never see her again?* Claire peers through the sheeting of rain now streaking across her windows – wait, there – a small figure under the bus shelter, a flash of baby pink. Claire pulls up next to the stop and sighs in relief as she sees Lacey. She is perched on the seat, knees curled up in front of her, head down. She looks up and shields her eyes with a hand. Claire realizes she still has her side spotlights on and hastily switches them off. She flicks on the internal light so that Lacey can see her face. Lacey's shoulders sag as she recognizes Claire, and the policewoman takes it as a sign of relief. The soaked girl opens the door and scurries in, like a cat who's been left out in the garden all night.

Claire lets Lacey sit silently and warm up for a while as they drive towards the estate where she lives. But she can't let her stay silent for ever.

'Are you going to tell me what's gone on?'

She glances at the girl and notices that her face is streaked with tears. 'I'm so sorry, Auntie Claire.'

'You never need to apologize to me, my love,' Claire says in a soft voice, a bloom of fierce love in her chest, 'you know that. I only want to make sure you're alright. Can you tell me what happened?'

'If I tell you, you can't tell anyone,' Lacey whispers.

'Love, you know I can't make promises like that.' She sighs.

Lacey sobs, and Claire places a hand on her knee. Lacey's leggings are cold and wet. Claire pulls over to the kerb and climbs out of the car, leaving the engine on and heater running. She walks to the boot and pulls out an old blanket that she keeps in her kit bag in case of emergency. She opens Lacey's door and wraps the blanket around her, tucking it in and under her knees. Lacey smiles weakly and Claire takes the opportunity to examine her face and smell her breath. No visible bruises. Alcohol.

She climbs back in to the driver's seat and turns to Lacey. 'I can promise you this. I won't tell anyone anything without telling you first. I won't tell anyone I don't have to tell, and anything I do will be with your best interests at heart.' She takes both of Lacey's hands in hers, ignoring the uncomfortable way the handbrake is digging into her kit belt as she leans between the seats. 'You know I love you.'

'And Mum?'

Claire pauses for just a second before nodding. 'And your mum.'

Lacey nods, sniffing hard.

'I snuck out to meet a boy.'

'Go on,' Claire says, gritting her teeth against the impulse to tell Lacey how incredibly stupid that was.

'He goes to my school. Year eleven. He said there was a party at his mate's house, but when we got there it was just him and his mate.' She wriggles her hands inside of Claire's, but doesn't pull them away. 'At first, it was fine. They were on his mate's Xbox and I had a go, then we listened to music. They kept giving me drinks.' Now that Claire's closer to her, she can smell the alcohol clearly. But Lacey isn't slurring, she doesn't seem drunk. *Year eleven*. That meant these boys were fifteen, sixteen. Claire clenches her jaw as Lacey continues. 'I had two beers, but I don't really like it. They kept trying to get me to drink more, but I said no.'

Claire nods encouragingly, a burst of pride that Lacey stuck to her guns and refused to drink more. It doesn't surprise her. The girl has seen what alcohol addiction has done to her mum.

'So, the boy, the one who goes to my school, he sends his mate downstairs to see if he can find some of his mum's wine for me to drink. I kept telling them that I didn't want a drink, that I was fine, but they didn't listen. They kept saying I needed to "chill".' Lacey pauses, wiping her nose with the blanket. 'Once his mate was gone, he started kissing me. I didn't mind at first, I liked him, but then he started putting his hands everywhere and pushing me into the sofa.' She begins to cry again.

'It's okay. You're safe now,' Claire says, rubbing Lacey's arm.

Lacey winces, and Claire pulls back the blanket. 'Are you hurt?' She runs her hands over Lacey's arms, up and around her shoulders, feeling the rakish edges of the shivering girl.

Lacey shakes her head. 'Just that arm, I think I bashed it on something as I ran out of the flat.'

Claire runs her eyes over the girl, noticing a tear in the high waistband of Lacey's leggings. Her blood runs cold.

'I kept telling him to stop but he wouldn't listen, he was pulling at my clothes so hard, I thought that I'd break.'

'Lacey.' Claire looks her in the eyes. 'I have to ask you this, love. Did he rape you?'

'No.' She says it firmly, shaking her head, and Claire believes her. 'I don't know what would have happened if I didn't manage to get him off me. Maybe – I think – I think he wanted to. I could feel his – it – his thingy, digging into my leg.'

Claire leans forward and hugs her goddaughter, the girl allowing herself to be pulled into the embrace and sobbing into Claire's shoulder.

'It's okay. I've got you.'

There's nothing she wants to do more than find out who these little fuckers are and pay them a visit with her team. The red mist throbs at the edges of her vision, and she takes a deep breath, letting it out low and quiet.

The police officer in her forces through, and she can't

resist a gentle prod. 'Are you going to tell me the names of these boys?'

Lacey's head shakes vigorously within her arms.

'Okay, love. Not now.' Lacey doesn't respond, keeping her face pushed into Claire's bosom.

Claire tells herself that, right now, she needs to be a godmother, not a copper.

'Okay, love. Let's get you home.'

Lacey opens the door to her mum's flat with the key she's had since she was six years old. Claire knows she's had it since she was six because she'd insisted June get one cut after Lacey was left on the doorstep for two hours in the rain, whilst June slept off a binge inside.

The flat is dark and smells like bin bags left out in the sun.

'Mum's been drinking again,' Lacey whispers.

Claire nods grimly. 'Get yourself to bed, I'll come up and check in on you before I leave.'

Lacey glances beyond Claire, into the living room. She looks as if she may protest, but then she yawns, lowering her shoulders, and begins to plod slowly up the stairs.

Claire walks into the dark sitting room, hit in the face by a strong smell of cigarette smoke. She can see a motionless mass on the sofa and flicks on the light. June is on her front, one leg and arm dangling from the sofa cushions onto the floor. She doesn't react to the light being switched on. She looks as though she's tripped, landed on the sofa and decided to stay there. Claire would consider checking her breathing, if she wasn't snoring loudly. There is an empty bottle of bargain-price vodka on its side on the carpet. The ashtray on the table is packed with dog-ends, and a long, thin plume of smoke curls upwards towards the ceiling from an errant butt. Claire walks over and picks it up, lifting it to her mouth and taking a long drag, before putting it out properly. She pushes the smoke out of her nose and considers June. She's obviously not been asleep long.

'June,' she says, 'wakey-wakey.'

She places the sole of her boot on her best friend's arse and pushes roughly. June's hanging arm and leg flop like overcooked noodles and she lets out a snort. When Lacey said June was out, she hadn't meant on the town. She's always been like this, Claire thinks, as she sits down on the armchair next to the sofa. She remembers brightly coloured alcopops in the park. How June never seemed to know her limit and would invariably end up vomiting or passing out. Or both. Claire hadn't minded when they were young. She never understood, though, how June could drink the way she did when she'd seen what it did to her father. He'd ended up in an early grave after a bar fight led to a heart attack. As they'd grown into adults together, Claire had learnt her limits. June had continued to push hers until nothing was off limits any more.

She glances at her watch and realizes that she's been out of action for over an hour. *Shit.* She gets up and walks into the kitchen. The smell of rubbish gets stronger and she grimaces as she looks at the piles of mouldy plates. She can't leave Lacey alone like this. She rummages in the cupboard under the sink until she finds a pair of rubber gloves.

Still sealed in their packet. She rips open the plastic, places them on the table and dials her inspector.

Fifteen

Claire has just finished a day shift and is walking to her car when a familiar figure catches her eye. Lacey is standing outside the corner shop. It's only been a few weeks since Claire has seen the girl. They've been short-staffed at work and Claire's been forced to pick up a lot of overtime, but Lacey looks as if she's grown taller even in that time. Her limbs have filled out, from the scraggly and awkward extremities of adolescence into graceful *almost* woman-hood. Claire stops on the pavement, smiling at Lacey's confident stance. Her hands are on her hips, and she's smiling at someone inside the shop. She's going to be a strong woman. As Claire watches, the door opens and a large man steps out. The smile slides from Claire's face as he puts an arm round Lacey and hands her a bottle of cheap alcohol. His hold is proprietary, his hands sliding down Lacey's back, closer and closer to her bottom. Lacey looks up at him, a dangerous shine in her eyes. Claire is upon them before she's really given any thought to moving and her mouth is open before her brain has caught up.

'What the fuck is this?'

Lacey stops in shock, her mouth falling open, and she hugs the vodka to her chest as if trying to make it disappear. The man frowns, looks Claire up and down, taking in her police-issue trousers, boots and shirt. She's taken off the epaulettes that hold her sergeant's stripes but it's still clear she is a copper.

His frown clears quickly and he steps forward, pushing Lacey back with his hand.

'Is there a problem, officer?'

His wide smile throws Claire for a second, and she looks from Lacey to the man, and back again, trying to make this scenario make sense. Trying to understand why he is so at ease.

'I'll say there's a problem,' she says, walking towards him. 'Is there a reason you're buying my fifteen-year-old goddaughter vodka?'

Lacey begins to talk, but the man holds up a finger and she snaps her mouth shut. A hot wave of disgust travels up through Claire's chest: *how dare he silence her like that?* In one swift move he lowers the finger and stretches out his hand. 'Ah! You must be the famous Auntie Claire.' He smiles. 'So glad to finally meet you.'

She narrows her eyes. She's met his type before, many times. So *calm*. So *reasonable*. It's the best way to get under her skin because she knows if she rises to it, she will be seen as the unreasonable one. She doesn't care. She ignores his hand, looks to Lacey. 'Are you alright, love?'

'Of course she's alright,' the man replies.

'I'm asking my goddaughter if she's alright, and you will let her answer.' She's the one pointing now, aiming her finger to the dead centre of his chest, where she'd quite like to see a bullet go. Everything about him gives her the creeps and every warning signal she has built in during her years of policing is screaming at her to get Lacey away from him. She looks pointedly at Lacey.

'Yes, Auntie Claire, I'm okay.' Her smile is wobbly.

'Lacey, why don't you introduce us?'

Lacey walks forward like a marionette and smiles at Claire. 'This is Craig.'

Craig puts a hand on Lacey's shoulder and Claire resists the urge to slap it away. 'And?' she asks, looking down at Lacey.

'And he's my . . .' Lacey's eyes stare into Claire's as she pauses, Craig squeezing her shoulder to push her onwards. 'He's my stepfather.'

The pavement seems to move beneath Claire's feet. She can't understand the words that are coming out of Lacey's mouth.

'And of course,' Craig begins, 'this isn't for Lacey!' He laughs at the ridiculousness of her assumption. 'It's for her mother and me. Now, come on, Lacey, let's get back to that gorgeous mother of yours.'

He steers Lacey around Claire, still frozen in shock. As they walk away, she pulls herself together. She watches as he keeps his hand on Lacey's shoulder, Lacey's head down, like a told-off child.

'Nope,' Claire says to herself, and jogs towards her car. She gets in and guns the engine, swinging the car out of its parking space and onto the road. She keeps her eyes on their backs until she has to turn away briefly to follow a small one-way system. If she times it right, she'll come out in front of them as they turn the corner towards June's house. *If that's where they're going. If he doesn't kidnap Lacey first.* She shakes her head and focuses on driving. *It can't be true. Her stepfather?*

After Claire had brought Lacey home in the middle of the night, around a year ago, she had dragged June back to AA. Claire had checked in on them every day, popping in before or after – or sometimes in the middle of – her shifts. She'd held June as she'd cried, the guilt racking through her in sobs, as she swore to change, swore to be a better mum. Claire had gone through the house from top to bottom, finding bottles hidden under the beds, at the back of wardrobes, buried beneath towels in the airing cupboard and even in a plant pot in the garden. She'd deep-cleaned, sorted, stacked and even helped June repaint the living room. June had been doing so well.

It's only a few weeks since I was there, Claire thinks, as she weaves through the traffic. *Only three weeks, surely?* But if she's honest it's probably longer. There's been so much overtime at work and she hasn't been able to say no to the money. Things are tight at home and she needs it. *Not more than four weeks, five?* As she's cursing herself for letting it go so long without visiting them *again, you shit excuse for a friend,* as she rounds the last corner and sees them. She breathes a sigh of relief and pulls up in their path.

'This ain't happening,' she says loudly as she climbs from the car. 'Lacey, get in.'

Lacey freezes and looks to Craig.

'Get in the car, Lacey,' Claire repeats.

Lacey walks to the car, but Craig grabs her by the arm. A tiny slip in his charming facade. 'Hang on now, what the hell do you think you're doing?'

'Let go of her arm, now.' Claire widens her stance and places her hands by her hips.

Craig drops Lacey's arm and Claire jerks her head to the girl, who opens the car door and slips inside. Claire closes the door for her before turning to face Craig.

'I don't know who you are, but you sure as fuck ain't any kind of father to her.'

He juts out his chin. 'We'll see what June says about that.'

'June is a raging alcoholic!' Claire shouts, looking to the bottle that's now in his hands. 'If you were any kind of stepfather or gave even one shit about her or Lacey, you wouldn't be bringing alcohol into that house.'

'She's fine, she can handle it.' He smirks, backing away and holding up his hands, the bottle of vodka sloshing as he does so. 'She'll tell you.'

'What's your surname?' Claire demands.

'Sorry, officer.' Craig begins to walk away. 'I've got places to be.'

'I'm taking Lacey home,' Claire shouts after him. 'And I wouldn't be turning up there any time soon, if you know what's good for you.'

He keeps walking. Claire takes a deep breath and climbs into the car.

*

She opens June's door with the key she's had for years.

'Upstairs,' she says to Lacey, and the girl obeys, her long legs taking the steps two at a time.

'Craig, darling.' June's voice floats out of the kitchen, a sing-song to her words. 'Is that you?'

It's true, then. Claire steadies herself on the banister for a moment, pinching the top of her nose and closing her eyes. A headache is suddenly squeezing her temples. *Stay calm. You won't get anywhere if you go in there shouting the odds.*

She straightens and walks into the kitchen. June is at the sink, a bright-pink apron at her waist, bubbles on her wrists. She turns, a huge smile on her face and a flush on her cheeks. There's an open bottle of wine on the table and place settings for two. She jumps as she sees Claire, the smile dropping from her face for a second, before she recovers herself.

'Claire,' she says brightly, 'what a nice surprise.'

The edges of her words are soft, her lipstick smudged.

'I just met Craig.' Claire grips the back of a kitchen chair, her knuckles turning white with the effort of remaining calm. 'He was in t'shops buying vodka with Lacey.'

'Oh yes.' June unties the apron and bundles it in her hands, twisting it as she speaks. 'Well, that's just for him, the vodka, I'm only having wine.'

'June, you know you can't *just* have wine.'

June grits her teeth and shoves the apron onto the table. 'I don't want to hear this right now, Claire. I know what you're going to say and I don't want to hear it.' She turns to the sink again and pulls the plug, so that Claire has to address her back.

'Where the fuck has this Craig bloke appeared from, then?'

'He makes me happy.'

'What?' Claire snorts, she can't help it. 'Happy enough that you've gone mad and married a bloody stranger? Brought him into this house – with your teenage daughter?'

June spins round. 'Married? We're not married. Where'd you get that idea?'

'Him!' Claire's voice is shrill now. 'He told me he was Lacey's stepfather – hands all over her he was. What was I supposed to think?' She laughs bitterly. 'Well, at least you've not married him, thank fuck!'

'We're engaged.' June's eyes are wide, and when Claire meets them, she looks at the floor.

'June, are you still going to your meetings?'

'That's where I met him, actually.'

'Of course it fucking is,' Claire says, rubbing her eyes with both hands. 'Are you still going or not?'

'We – well, we both stopped going – we decided we'd support each other.' June walks to Claire and takes her hands. 'Honestly, Claire, if you just listen to him, he's got some great ideas, he's been doing this technique for years, where he can have a little alcohol every night but not go mad, y'know? It really works, I've only been having wine and I've been fine – I feel great!' June's eyes are wild and she looks at Claire like a child trying to convince an adult to let her have the biscuit jar.

Claire can smell the alcohol on her breath. 'June, you know you can't do this. You've tried to cut back before. You can't do it like that, June, you're an alcoholic.'

'I fucking know that.' June drops Claire's hands and backs away, her voice reaching a rasping shout. 'Don't you think I don't know that! I just want to have fun, he makes me feel good about myself, I just—'

Claire cuts her off with a sweep of her arm, pointing upstairs. 'And what about Lacey? What about your fifteen-year-old daughter, June? Do you think it's *fun* for her? Having you drinking again, you and this fucking bear of a man in her house?'

'Lacey loves Craig!' June lights up at the idea. 'Here, she'll tell you.' She begins shouting for Lacey to come down, and Claire sinks into a seat. Her head is pounding and she feels wrung out.

A few seconds later, Lacey skulks into the kitchen. She looks at her mother, lipstick smudged and wonky eyeliner, and her face creases in disgust.

'Lace, tell Auntie Claire how nice Craig is.'

Lacey rolls her eyes.

'Come on, Lace, honey, didn't he buy you those shoes?'

Lacey nods. 'He's pretty generous.'

'Lacey, you know I love you, kid, but this is between your mum and me.' Claire looks to June and shakes her head. 'Relying on your *child* to tell me that your current boy-friend, sorry fiancé' – she mimes air quotes sarcastically – 'is alright, is really not helping your case.'

'I'm not a fucking case!' June roars, making Lacey and

Claire jump. 'I'm not a fucking case for you to solve!' She waves her arms and grabs the bottle of wine, swigging directly from the bottle. 'You turn up here, always trying to *fix me*, well, what if I can't be fixed? What if I don't want to be?'

'Lacey,' Claire says, 'go upstairs.'

'No,' Lacey says, and now she is shouting too, red-faced fury directed at her mother. 'Craig doesn't treat me like a child! He's not even here for you, you stupid bitch. A drunken wreck who can't even put her make-up on properly, as if!'

The room stills and Claire's blood freezes in her veins. Lacey's words echo in the air – *he's not even here for you*. June continues to swig from the wine bottle, whilst Claire stares at Lacey.

Tears are rolling down Lacey's face. Her shoulders shaking. She wipes her nose and says, 'He loves me.'

Claire wraps her arms around the girl and brings her to the kitchen table, pushing her gently into a chair. She sits next to her, pulling her small hands into her lap. 'Sweetheart, I know you think he loves you, and I know that at fifteen you feel old enough to agree to love him back, but you're still a child.'

Lacey continues to cry.

'I think you're so upset because, deep down, you know that it's not right for an adult to love a child the way Craig says he loves you.' She watches the small girl in front of her, relief mixed with sadness as she starts to nod. As if she's just been waiting for someone to notice.

Claire can sense that June has gone stock-still behind

them. She turns to her friend. June's face is pale, her mouth in such a tightly closed line it looks as if it's been stitched shut.

'You fucking liar.' She spits each word at Lacey, like venom, and then begins to shout. Words that a mother should never call her own daughter. Words that were made up by men, centuries ago, to shame women.

Claire pulls Lacey up and walks her into the hall. 'Get your stuff, you're coming home with me.'

As Lacey runs up the stairs, Claire walks back into the kitchen. June appears to have spent herself, she's sunk into a chair, but she looks up defiantly at Claire, a spark of fight still in her. She juts out her chin and says, 'She's always made things up.'

Claire folds her arms and looks at her oldest friend. She takes a deep breath, biting back every awful word she wants to throw at her. Instead, her voice comes out low.

'You think you know people.' She sighs. 'Every time I think you've sunk to the lowest you can go, you prove me wrong. But I never thought you, of all people, would choose a man over your own daughter.'

June's face crumples but Claire's seen it all before. She turns and walks out of the kitchen.

PC Claire Lesley chose Lacey that day. Chose the girl, over her oldest friend. It took everything she had to walk away from June. Sometimes, in the years that followed, she doubted that decision, but then she thought back to that day in June's kitchen. She'd known that the real June was gone.

Lost. She'd known then, and she knows now, that if the real June had been there that day, the June of her childhood, that she would've wanted Claire to choose Lacey too.

Claire went on to officially foster Lacey, with June's permission. Three years later, when Lacey was eighteen, June was found dead at home after suffering a huge heart attack. Her heart was determined to have been damaged irreparably during years of alcohol and drug abuse. The death was deemed to be non-suspicious. A year after that, Claire adopted Lacey.

PC Claire Lesley served thirty years in the Yorkshire Police Service. She progressed to the rank of Sergeant, and worked in many different units, including specializing in domestic abuse and sexual offences. She spent part of her career working in the homicide department, as a Family Liaison Officer. She received two Chief Constable's Commendations, and the Police Long Service and Good Conduct Medal. When asked to sum up her career, she stated, *'Policing is a career like no other, and I'm privileged to have been able to have a long and happy career. I'd certainly encourage women to join policing, these days we can accomplish just as much as the men – sometimes even more!'*

Chapter 9

Domestic murder is one of the world's most common crimes, and it's almost exclusively committed against women. Older, even, than prostitution, it's a type of murder that is so prevalent, it is almost accepted as normal. The sad truth is that no one is shocked when a woman is killed by a man she knows.

Invisible women exist in houses across the UK. In *Happy Valley*, Joanna Hepworth is the perfectly written, fictitious example of an invisible woman. She's coercively controlled by her violent husband, Rob Hepworth, who has subjected her to years of shocking violence. Often, in real-life cases of domestic murder, the female victim's voice is unheard, forgotten amidst the chase to find and punish the suspect.

The vulgar details of the crime will be reported in detail, over and over again, both in court and in the papers, but who really remembers the victim?

It's the critical role of the family liaison officer to bring these women back to life, to present their lives – the dreams and futures cut short – in front of a jury. Whilst FLOs are firstly, and most importantly, detectives, they are also required to provide a more caring side to policing. They provide emotional support as well as policing expertise. They are trained to investigate the victim's life from the inside, whilst remaining professional and impartial. But these detectives are also human, and it's difficult to maintain emotional distance during some murder investigations, as DC Emily Rogers discovered during her long career as a family liaison officer.

Detective Constable Emily Rogers hangs up the phone, stands and begins to gather her things. She's in the police station where she works, in a large, open-plan office assigned to the Murder Squad. She pockets her mobile, slips her laptop and notepad into her handbag and grabs her family liaison officer 'go bag'. Inside should be everything an FLO needs: evidence bags and packaging supplies, early evidence kits, DNA swabs, statement paper, and her own personal additions – teabags, biscuits, spare pens and tissues.

She's just been assigned to a new case. Uniformed officers are on the scene of a murder, and there's a suspect in custody. She pops into the control room on her way out of the building to get a printout of the incident report. She reads it as she walks to her car.

14:34 Inft called and stated that there was a man in his shop saying that he's killed his wife. The man has now left but the shopkeeper knows who he is. There was shouting and the line was dropped

14:34 F62 assigned and en route

14:41 Officers at scene

14:45 F62 requesting officers attend 21 Meadow Lane – home address of male suspect – urgent response requested

14:46 F63 assigned to home address

14:58 Officers at scene 21 Meadow Lane

14:59 F63 requesting more units please

15:00 F60 assigned – travelling time from town centre – on blues

15:14 From F63 – female found deceased at address. Suspicious death confirmed. PC3571 beginning crime scene log. Requesting more officers to control crime scene – family members being obstructive – please inform duty inspector, coroner, CSI and CID

Emily scans the rest of the printout, but there's nothing that can give her any further insight into what has happened and why. It's 5 p.m. now, CID will have attended to confirm that the case is a suspected murder, and will have then called her squad. She was assigned by her detective chief inspector, DCI Briggs. He informed her that the suspect is in custody, and that the victim's family had already been informed – they'd heard what had happened through the community grapevine and had turned up at the house. As for possible motive, as usual, she'll be going into the situation blind.

Each new FLO job brings its own unique challenges, you never know what you will face when you arrive at the scene. If you asked Emily to describe her job, she'd say that a family liaison officer is firstly an investigator. She's primarily a detective. She's also there to facilitate communication between the police and the family, to support the family, and to record as accurately as possible the information she obtains from, and the observations she makes about, the relatives.

That would be her official answer. The reality of the role is much harder for her to define. It's breaking bad news. It's giving the relatives agency in the decisions around their loved one's body and possessions. It's listening to the sound of their hearts breaking at the morgue, when their last shred of hope gets ripped away. It's holding back the tears when they can't. It's holding hands, making tea and knowing when to fade into the background.

Emily climbs into her car and begins to drive to the address. Anticipation builds as she gets closer; the fear of not knowing what to expect threatens to overwhelm her, the thought of another family's grief making her wonder if she should turn back. She keeps driving. There's a woman at the house she's going to that's at risk right now of becoming a number. Another woman killed by the very man supposed to care for her the most. Yes, she's there for the family, but the real reason Emily does this time and again, faces the repeated vicarious trauma, is for the victim. She may be the only one who can give this victim a voice. She can remind everyone, if the case goes to court, that this victim was a woman. A woman with hopes, dreams and a life that was cruelly taken away from her.

Emily pulls up to the address. The front door is open and a uniformed PC stands outside. She climbs out of her car and assesses the front of the property. It's a small, terraced house, on a street of similar properties. The windows are dirty at the corners and the curtains are drawn. She's relieved that she doesn't have to inform the family. Although she's done it many times, it's something that she's never got used to. She looks again to the windows of the house and thinks about death messages that she's had to give before. How she would sit outside in the car, mentally preparing herself. Sometimes, she could see family life carrying on as normal through open blinds. She remembers watching a family preparing to sit down to dinner, their dining room illuminated by the lights inside. The mum placing dishes in the middle of the table whilst the dad laid out the cutlery. A teenager laughing with a younger child. She could hear their joy through the summer air, their windows open in the heat. Emily had stood in the darkness, knowing that she was going to bring it in with her. Knowing that this moment was the last one they would have before their world was shattered. Their 24-year-old son had been killed in a road traffic collision.

She shakes the memory away and walks up the path to the door, giving her name and collar number to the PC with the crime scene log.

'The body's been taken. Forensics are still in there,' he says, and points to the pile of plastic-wrapped forensic clothing next to him. Emily pulls on a white paper suit and slips blue plastic booties over her shoes, before snapping a mask over her nose and mouth.

'Thanks.' Emily nods and heads inside.

She steps to the ingress. She can hear soft talking ahead of her, in what she imagines to be the kitchen area.

'FLO! Okay to come in?' she calls from the outside step.

'Yes, all good,' comes the reply. 'Stick to the approach path, please.'

'Will do,' she shouts, as she carefully steps along the metal footplates that have been set out along the hallway. The taste of copper fills the air as she approaches the kitchen and she grimaces, knowing that the scene is going to be gory. She rounds the corner, pushing herself forwards, when what she really wants to do is back-pedal.

There is blood everywhere. A crime scene technician is squatting by a kitchen cupboard with a swab and looks up as Emily stands in the doorway.

'It's a gruesome one, I'm afraid. She was found in there.' She points to the tall cupboard that Emily is standing next to, located just outside the kitchen door. It looks like an airing cupboard. Emily takes a step away from it.

The CSI gets up, a small groan escaping her lips as she straightens her legs. She walks towards the cupboard and opens it. Emily leans forward so that she can see inside. It houses a squat water tank, and the shelves above it are stacked with towels and linens. There is blood streaked on the floor around the tank, and a pool of blood in one corner. It seems to have dripped from somewhere above, and settled. A clump of long, black hair is visible in the hinge of the door.

A voice from behind her makes her jump, and she turns to see a second CSI.

'Sorry,' he says, 'I was going to say, it looks like he's used multiple weapons to kill her. She has two knives still in situ.' He points to the floor behind them, where a hammer and a metal bar have been seized and packaged. They are propped up against the wall. Emily can see that they're heavily bloodstained.

'Poor woman,' murmurs Emily.

She excuses herself from where the CSIs are working and follows the footplates into the sitting room. More blood. She's glad of the mask she's wearing and wishes they would invent one that cuts odours. As a detective, her job is to start at the centre of the victim's life. This was her home. She looks around the room. It's messy, the surfaces full of empty cartons, plates, bulging ashtrays and crumbs. The carpet looks as if it hasn't been hoovered in some time, and children's toys are scattered everywhere. On the mantelpiece there are a number of family photos, and she draws closer to have a look. In each picture is a man, sometimes with the children, mostly alone. He is in various places – sightseeing, holidays, religious festivals. She searches for a woman's face amongst the photographs but it's not there. She still doesn't know what the victim looks like. After a brief look around the rest of the house, the bedrooms simply furnished, the bathroom filthy, she heads back outside.

'Do you know who was first on scene?' she asks the officer guarding the property.

He gives her the collar numbers of two female officers. Tells her that they're back at the nick with the murder suspect. The tone of his voice tells her that he's jealous that they got to arrest a murder suspect whilst he's stuck guarding the scene.

'Well done on the log,' she says, nodding to the crime scene log in his hands, 'it's very neat.'

He stands a little straighter as she walks away.

Back at the nick, she hunts down the officers who were first on scene. She finds them in the canteen.

'Rebecca!' she says, recognizing one of them instantly.

'Em.' Rebecca smiles, standing up and drawing Emily into a hug.

'Rough one today?' Emily says.

'Tell me about it.' Rebecca shakes her head. 'And Shabnam here has only been in eight weeks.'

The other officer glances up at Emily and gives a watery smile. She's holding her mug so hard her knuckles are white.

'Baptism of fire.' Emily nods in sympathy.

She takes a seat at the same table and asks Rebecca to give her the details of the call.

'So, the first we hear, there's a bloke at the shops saying he's topped his wife.' Rebecca leans back in her chair, ready to get it all out. 'We're told to go to this bloke's address. When we get there, there's this group of men outside. The front door's open and they're all arguing, we couldn't understand a thing they were saying as they're all speaking a foreign language, but obviously something's gone on. Before we can find out what's happening the bloke turns up, he's run back from the shops, and he's trying to get back in the house.

'It was chaos.' Rebecca looks to Shabnam, who nods in agreement. 'So me and Shab have got ourselves between the men and the front door, and I'm asking what's happened, but the men are just shouting over us. There was a lot of angry arm-waving, not necessarily at us, but I could see it getting out of hand – plus, we've got a potential murder scene behind us that needed protecting. I've called for more units, but it's so loud I can't tell if anyone's been assigned or not.'

'From the incident log, it looks like another unit was assigned, but they were travelling from town,' Emily clarifies.

Rebecca tuts. 'Typical. Anyway, we identify that the bloke who's run back from the shops is the husband, and he's *desperate* to get back inside. At first, he's pretending to be concerned about his wife, saying he needs to check on her. When that doesn't work, he starts spouting all this shit – *she's my wife, what has this got to do with you? – this is my house, you can't stop me going in there* – the usual.'

'We knew we had to get in there, like, she could still be alive,' Shabnam adds, looking to Rebecca for approval.

'Absolutely.' Rebecca nods. 'So basically, I just shut the door on them. I grab Shab, shove her inside and slam it in their faces. I was shouting something along the lines of this being a crime scene and that if they came in, they'd be arrested, but God knows whether they'd listen to me anyway. I got the sense that they weren't used to listening to a woman.

'We're inside, and I tell Shab to put the deadbolt across and make sure no one comes through the door. Then I went to look for her.' Rebecca falls silent and Shabnam stares into her hot chocolate.

'Go on,' Emily says.

'I knew, you know? I knew she was dead. Something about the stillness of the place. I glanced into the sitting room and saw all the blood, then looked into the kitchen. More blood. The airing-cupboard door was open a crack, and I don't know what made me open it, but – I found her.' She shakes her head, then looks up at Emily with such a fierce expression of anger on her face that Emily's eyes prickle. 'He'd covered her with dirty rugs and stacked bags of rubbish on top of her, but I could see her hair. I got the stuff off her to check if she was alive, but as soon as I saw her face, I knew she'd been dead for a few hours, at least. The way she was shoved in – well, you've seen the cupboard, I expect – I would have said for certain that you couldn't fit a person in there.

'He had killed her in the most horrific way,' Rebecca

says, her voice breaking slightly. She clears her throat and continues. 'There were knives impaled in each breast – one in each – and she was bound and gagged. There were so many injuries, I couldn't tell which one had killed her.'

'She was stuffed in there like rubbish,' Shabnam says.

'I update Dispatch, ask them to call everyone they need to call. We're just about to have a look upstairs when shouting starts up again outside. I can hear a woman's voice, so we go back out. Her family had turned up . . .' Rebecca pauses, shaking her head again. 'It was her sister – the victim's – her sister's husband, and various other women from the community. They were hysterical. I had to tell the sister right there on the doorstep. She fell into my arms.'

'It was awful,' Shabnam says, her eyes glistening.

'So, the family found out pretty quickly.' Emily makes a note in her book. 'What did you think of the husband?'

'He honestly acted as if he didn't know what all the fuss was about. He was shaking his head, I could hear him talking to the other men he had with him – apparently, they were his family, brothers, cousins, et cetera. The victim's sister started screaming at him, shouting *how dare you*. I asked one of the women with her what he was saying, and she told me he was telling his brothers what an awful wife she was.' Rebecca tuts. 'Like she deserved it.'

'He thinks of her as a possession,' Emily guesses.

'That's very much how it seems.'

'Anything else?'

'That's it. We arrest him on suspicion of murder, and here we are.'

It's the next day, and Emily is standing in the morgue. She's used to the chill of the room but she doesn't think she'll ever get used to the odour. It reminds her of the smell of her old school chemistry lab, with an undercurrent of raw meat.

The autopsy is about to begin. Rebecca is standing next to Emily, at the foot of the autopsy table. Her duty here is to provide continuity – to confirm that the body on the table is the same body she found in the airing cupboard at 21 Meadow Lane. She affirms that it is, and leaves the room, her involvement with this murder case finished until it gets to court. Emily looks down at the body, which has now been confirmed as belonging to thirty-year-old Iraqi woman, Hajar al-Mutairi.

Hajar is beautiful. Though her face is badly bruised on one side, Emily can see that she has elegant, symmetrical features. She has a cluster of small scars around her eyes, the bridge of her nose and eyebrows, in various stages of healing. She wishes she had met her when she was alive. Wishes she could have stopped this from happening. Emily pulls her arms behind her back and clamps her hands together. Legs slightly apart and shoulders back, she assumes a *police-officer's stance*. Sometimes it's the only thing that stops her from losing it.

Hajar is naked on the table. She was partially clothed when found in the cupboard, in filthy jogging bottoms and torn knickers. The clothes were bloody, but the knickers also had old blood stains in them, as if Hajar had bled in them regularly. Emily wonders why the knickers weren't thrown away and replaced. Hajar's body is hard to look at. Dr Elkins, the pathologist, has estimated that she has at least 150 injuries, although the real number will be confirmed once he is finished. Emily looks to Hajar's breasts. The knives have been removed, leaving small holes in their wake. Her nipples are covered in lurid bite marks, and Emily finds that she is gritting her teeth. An ache starts in the side of her jaw, but she can't seem to relax it.

The assorted tools, thought to have been used as weapons, that were found around the house have been laid in a sterilized tray next to the table. Four knives of different sizes, a drill, a hammer, a length of wood and two metal bars. One of the bars is bent. The pathologist will try to match them to injuries to Hajar's body.

'This is going to take some time,' Dr Elkins says, looking to Emily and his assistant. They both nod grimly. Emily looks to the body map in her hands, where she is to mark every injury for her notes; her pen hovers over it impotently.

She doesn't know where to start.

Dr Elkins pulls off his gloves with a sigh. 'This is one hundred per cent a case of *overkill*. In fact, I don't think I've ever seen a body that has been so ferociously attacked.'

Emily nods and notes *overkill* in her notebook. It's a term that's used to describe attacks, usually domestic, where the suspect has used force far greater than they needed to kill someone. It can be a sign of rage, or mental illness, or extreme hatred or disrespect to the victim. It's certainly not something you should be able to do to someone you loved.

'There are 290 separate injuries. Many of them are at different stages of healing. She's obviously been being beaten regularly, for a long time. She would have suffered greatly. Cause of death . . .' He pauses. 'I'm leaning towards a combination of blood loss from multiple stab wounds and blunt force trauma. She has a massive amount of injury to a number of internal organs. I'll get you my official report as soon as I can.'

'Thank you,' Emily says.

'There's a specific test I want done on her heart – it needs to go to a specialist in Leeds.' He hands her a cool box. 'The name and address is on the label, they're expecting you.'

'Of course.' Emily nods, glancing at the neatly written label on the top of the box. 'I'll get it over there now.'

Emily leaves the morgue, her precious cargo gripped in both hands. She places the box gently on the passenger seat of her car. She wonders if putting the seat belt around it is silly, then decides that she doesn't care if it's silly or not, she wants each part of Hajar to be treated with respect, and she straps the box in.

She pulls out of the car park and heads in the direction of the city. She glances to the box beside her, imagining what she'll say when her husband asks her what she did today. *I carried a heart around in a cool box.* Maybe not. As she travels to the specialist, all she can see is Hajar's face, pale and mottled on the table. She'd still not been able to find any photographs of the woman, so she's never had an opportunity to see what she looked like in life. As she parks up next to the lab where the heart is due to be deposited, she places her hand on the cool box.

I will make sure that they know who you were. I will give you a voice.

Emily stands in Hajar and Hussein's bedroom. She has decided to spend a whole day at the house, which is still closed to the family as a crime scene, and therefore empty. She has to get a feel for Hajar's life. She has to make sure that the jury sees her as a person, instead of just another immigrant, just another beaten woman. It never makes sense to Emily how domestic murders are somehow viewed by the public as more *acceptable*, less *frightening* than stranger murders. Surely there isn't anything more terrifying than not even being safe in your own home? Surely there's nothing more horrendous than being killed by those closest to you? Your own family?

The atmosphere inside the home is heavy. Despite all of the curtains having been opened, it feels dark, like the darkness is seeping from the walls rather than being present due to a lack of light. Emily rubs her arms and realizes she has goosebumps. She's not superstitious, but if she was, she'd be certain that Hajar was standing next to her. Emily's role is to give Hajar a voice in court, and she's decided to start at the centre of her life, and work outwards. This is where she spent nearly all of her time. What will it reveal about her? Emily moves around the bedroom, opening drawers and cupboards. She has brought a colleague with her for the day, another experienced FLO. Gemma is standing by the door. They're both wearing gloves.

'I've just been in the bathroom,' Gemma says, 'there's something very odd.'

'Apart from how filthy it is?' Emily asks.

'Yeah, apart from that.' Gemma puts a hand on one hip and tilts her head. 'There's literally no women's products in there at all.'

'I was about to come and say exactly the same thing to you,' Emily says, pointing to the bed. 'Look, there's a bedside table, but only on one side. It's full of Hussein's things by the looks of it. The other side, presumably where Hajar slept – nothing.'

Emily moves across to a tall chest of drawers that comes up to just under her chest. 'And look at all the bottles on here – all men's products. Aftershave, face lotion, body spray. There's only one mirror, that's on the inside door of the wardrobe.' Emily opens the door so that Gemma can see inside. 'Which is full of men's clothes. *Only* men's.'

Gemma has moved to the drawers and is searching through them. She grimaces as she picks her gloved fingers between rolled-up boxer shorts. 'Where is all her underwear?'

Emily shakes her head, taking the lid off the bulging wash basket in the corner. More men's clothes. She spots the edges of a plastic bin bag shoved behind the wash basket. 'Hang on,' she says, 'what's in here?'

She pulls the bin bag into the centre of the room and opens the top. Inside is a small pile of neatly folded clothes. She lays each item out on the bed. Two large T-shirts, stained. One pair of navy tracksuit bottoms, with paint splatters on them, like something you'd wear to decorate. Brown stains around one ankle. One grey – possibly originally white – and worn bra. And three pairs of knickers. One pair looks well washed but unstained. The other two have what look likes blood stains to the gussets.

'They look like period stains,' Gemma suggests.

'You're right,' Emily says, considering the underwear. 'They look exactly like when you've soaked through a pad or tampon. But why has she kept these?'

'Maybe they were all she had? We've not seen any other women's clothing, have we?'

Emily looks inside the bin bag again. 'Wait, I've missed something.' She tips the bag out, upside down, over the bed. A small bundle of nappies falls out.

'Nappies?'

Emily picks one of them up. It's clean, unused, but it's been cut up, into strips.

'What is she doing with nappies?'

'She was using them as sanitary towels.' Emily suddenly understands, as the devastating reality of Hajar's life hits her in the chest. 'Were there any sanitary products in the bathroom?'

'No,' Gemma says. 'She didn't even have a toothbrush.'

The two women are silent for a moment. Emily tries to imagine what her life would be like without access to her own clothes, to sanitary products, make-up. A deep rage burns in her chest, and an idea begins to take shape in her mind. 'We need to show just how horrendous her life was,' she says, her heart beating faster. 'We need to compare everything he has with everything she hasn't. Make the jury really see what it was like for her here. How he kept her like a slave.'

She lays the strips of nappy next to the clothes. 'We need to photograph everything.'

Later on, after they've taken their photographs, they sit in the car and eat lunch.

'You know, this couple have lived in this street for nearly five years, and I can't find one person, outside of her direct family, who knew Hajar. Not one person.'

'She wasn't allowed out,' Gemma says, through a mouthful of sandwich.

'It seems that way.' Emily shakes her head. 'It's nearly impossible to pull together victimology, antecedence, or anything that I usually can. This case is totally unique.'

'Thank God.'

'She's not registered at the doctor's, the local chemist has no records of her, she wasn't working but not registered to receive any benefits. No one in the local shops has seen her. I spoke to the women who live next door.' Emily points to the house directly next to Hussein's. 'They're refugees from Sudan and they're terrified of police. They didn't open the door to any of the neighbour enquiries. Not until it was just me.' She turns to face Gemma. 'They heard it all. They told me it sounded like he was torturing her to death. They'd been hearing shouting for ages, absolutely ages. They said they used to cry for her, that it sounded that bad that they'd actually cry.' Emily sighs in despair. 'One of them said to me that it had been so silent for the last few days that they suspected she was dead.'

'God,' Gemma exclaims. 'But they didn't tell anyone?'

'No.' Emily shakes her head. 'They're just terrified of authority. And of Hussein and his family, by the sound of it. They have agreed to give evidence at court.'

'That's something, I suppose.'

'They said they would occasionally see her in the garden, that they tried to ask her if she needed help, but every time she would be called back inside. They hadn't seen her in months.' Emily considers if she feels angry with the women for not calling, and decides that she does, but she also understands why they didn't.

'I can't even find any photos of her.' Emily throws up her hands. 'Literally the only photo I've found is that awful one on her passport. It's so devoid of personality, her expression blank. Her sister's told me that she didn't even want to come to the UK. She knew she'd be even more isolated here. She wanted to stay within her community.'

'No photos, in this age of social media,' Gemma muses, 'imagine that. I take it she didn't have a phone?'

'Of course not. No access to the internet. No access to real life. Her life was lived within those four walls.'

They both look at the unimposing terraced house.

'Better get back to it,' Gemma says, scrunching up her crisp packet and shoving it into the passenger-door pocket.

'And they wonder why police cars are in such a state,' Emily quips.

'Yeah, yeah.' Gemma laughs, climbing out of the car.

'Come and have a look at this,' Emily calls.

Gemma walks in from the kitchen and looks over Emily's shoulder.

'Five optician's receipts.' Emily frowns. 'All in Hajar's name. This is literally the first time I've seen her name written on anything except her passport. All in the last year.'

'Who needs to go to the optician's that much?'

Emily thinks back to the morgue. The scars around Hajar's eyes. She closes her own eyes and whispers, 'He kept breaking her glasses when he beat her.'

Gemma puts a warm hand on her shoulder. 'We're nearly done now. Let me follow up with the optician's. You need a break.'

After dropping Gemma home, Emily sits at the traffic lights in her unmarked police car. She is sobbing. Ugly crying. Large, chest-racking sobs and snot and spit. A horn sounds from behind her, and she realizes the lights have turned green. She drives slowly through the intersection and pulls off to the side of the road, her vision too blurry to drive safely. She sits in her car and cries.

Once she is spent, she fishes the large box of tissues out

of the glove compartment and wipes her face. She opens the window and drives towards her house, allowing the cold air to cool her hot and swollen eyes.

By the time she gets home all signs of her grief will be hidden neatly away in the folds of her warrant card.

The next day, Emily visits Hajar's family.

'My sister was kind. She was beautiful. When we were little, she always said that she wanted to be a teacher when she grew up.' Mariam holds a tissue to her nose, her voice thick with tears. 'I hate him for what he did to her.'

'I'm so sorry,' Emily says.

They are sitting in Mariam's kitchen, six weeks after the murder of her sister, Hajar.

'I know it may be difficult to talk about her, but I really need to get a sense of her as a person, what her life was like, so that I can show the jury who she was.'

Mariam nods vigorously. 'It's not hard to talk about her. I want to. I feel like no one here wants to talk about it. My husband tells me to stop crying; our parents are so upset, I feel like I can't talk about her with them.'

This is the fourth or fifth time Emily has spoken to Mariam. As an FLO, you realize that every family is different, everyone needs to grieve in a different way. It's not uncommon for bereaved family members to take a while to warm up to you – to trust you. A good FLO can make the family open up to them, so that every area of a victim's life can be examined. It's often the family secrets that point to murder motives. Mariam has been open from the start.

Emily gets the feeling that she's grateful to be finally talking about what Hajar's life was really like.

'We were so worried about her.' She points to the sitting room, where her mother and father are seated. 'My father was trying to arrange a divorce. It's something that has to be approved – in our culture – by the senior member of the community, and him – Hussein,' – she shudders at the sound of his name – 'he'd nearly agreed. My father had to offer to pay him for his trouble.' She begins to sob lightly. 'But we were too late.'

Emily puts a hand over Mariam's, allows the woman to cry. After a couple of minutes, she blows her nose and wipes her eyes, before her eyes widen and she sits up. 'Do you know that she called them – our parents – the night before he killed her?'

Emily leans forward; this is information that she hasn't heard before.

'What did she say?'

'She'd managed to beg a phone from Hussein's mother, and she spoke to my father. She told him that Hussein was getting worse, that he was beating her more often. She asked him to help her. We all knew that he was abusive, but in our culture – it's hard to explain – a husband is allowed to discipline his wife. But even for our culture, what he was doing was becoming unacceptable.'

Emily nods encouragingly.

'She told him something strange – she said to look on top of the kitchen cupboards.' Mariam frowns. 'Why would she say that?'

Emily understands immediately. The forensics team had found a plastic carrier bag on top of one of the kitchen cupboards, full of long black hair. When they had examined it in the lab, they had discovered that the clumps of hair were attached to pieces of scalp. The theory was that Hussein had been pulling out Hajar's hair, and that she had been trying to save it, as a way to prove his abuse against her. The woman was clever. Emily's chest feels tight, as she realizes that Hajar probably knew what was going to happen to her. Or feared it, at least.

'That's really helpful.' She squeezes Mariam's hand. 'All of this information is so helpful, Mariam, thank you. You're doing really well. I will look into that for you.'

Emily doesn't want to interrupt Mariam's recollections of her sister's life by telling her about the bag of hair. She will have to tell Hajar's family about it at some point – part of being an FLO is being as transparent as possible – when suitable to do so.

'Did she say anything else?'

'She told him,' Mariam takes a deep breath, 'she said, *I think I'm going to die.* The last words she said to him, the last words she ever said to our father, were *pray for me.*'

She begins to cry again, pressing a tissue to her mouth as though to muffle herself. Emily can tell that it's because she doesn't want to upset her parents. Her mother is heavily sedated and her father spends most of his time staring blankly at the television.

'We were all worried sick about her,' Mariam says, after regaining her composure. 'We were determined to get her out of there – we should have just gone round and taken her. I wish we would have. But my father was worried about repercussions that our family might face, the repercussions Hajar would face. We were hardly allowed to see her. We hadn't seen her for six months, before that day.'

'He was isolating her,' Emily offers.

'Yes, he was. We should have stopped him.'

'It's not your fault. The only person to blame here is Hussein.'

'And his family.'

'Yes.' Emily nods. 'It does seem that they were aware of how badly she was being treated.'

'She had asked Hussein's mother for help. Do you know what she said?' Mariam asks, wiping the corners of her eyes with a screwed-up tissue. When she speaks, her words come out hard and angry. 'Why don't you just try harder to be a better wife?'

They fall silent for a moment, Emily digesting the cruelty of Hussein's family. Mariam sips on a glass of water. Emily takes the opportunity to ask Mariam some questions about Hajar's habits.

'I want to show you some photos of the house,' Emily begins, and Mariam's eyes go wide. 'Don't worry, there's no – *don't say blood* – evidence, in the photos, it's just the house. I want to see what you think, it was very unkempt when we found Hajar.'

Mariam holds out her hands, and Emily passes her four photos. Emily took them when she spent a day there, trying to get to know Hajar. She'd deliberately avoided capturing the blood stains. The photos show the unwashed plates in the kitchen, the dirty clothes strewn around the bedrooms, and the filthy carpets. Mariam flicks through the photos, immediately beginning to shake her head.

'What are these? This is not her house?'

Emily assures her that it is.

'This is not right. No, no, Hajar was extremely house-proud. Hussein would constantly berate her to clean, but she always kept it clean anyway, it was impeccable the last time I saw it!' Mariam is clearly shocked.

'When was the last time you were there?'

'Around a year ago, I think.'

So, Emily thinks, the housekeeping – which Hajar was solely responsible for – had declined significantly over a year. Was it because she was beaten so regularly that she physically couldn't look after the house any more? Mariam is looking intently at Emily, and seems to read her mind.

She covers her mouth and whispers, 'Oh, Allah.'

'I know how difficult this must be, Mariam, but I need to show you the clothing she was wearing when she died.'

Mariam nods, tears forming in the corners of her eyes. Her hand is still gripped to her mouth as Emily slides a photo across the table. In the photo is a pair of grey jogging bottoms. They are unbranded, with bloodstaining around the thighs and groin. The rest of the bottoms are caked in dirt.

'She can't have been wearing these.' Mariam's voice shakes. 'She can't. These are not her. She was always clean, she was graceful – beautiful.'

'I'm sorry,' Emily says, for the hundredth time. It sounds hollow.

In court, Hussein's defence against a lot of the accusations was that his family were poor. That neither of them had lived a good life, that both of them were struggling. Emily had spent hours compiling detailed photos and notes of his life, compared to Hajar's. These included images of the branded clothes in his wardrobe, the expensive sportswear in his drawers. His expensive iPhone contract and his busy social life. Also found at the house was a suitcase of women's plastic and rubber sexual cosplay outfits. They were all in Hajar's size. The jury saw that Hussein wouldn't buy clean knickers for his wife but he would happily pay to dress her up like a sex doll. The optician that Hajar had visited, supervised by Hussein, of course, confirmed that she had attended, again and again, with eye injuries and broken glasses. The neighbours confirmed her screams.

The crime scene examiners had described their theory as to what happened to Hajar on the evening she died. Blood-spatter analysis experts explained how the stains high and low on the living room walls showed that Hajar had tried to stand on multiple occasions. How she had fallen. How she had tried to escape Hussein by pulling herself up and along on furniture and the walls. Despite her attempts to escape, Hussein had beaten and stabbed her with numerous tools and instruments. The bent metal bar found at the crime scene was believed to have been bent by the force of him beating her. The final cause of death was found to be blood loss and blunt force trauma.

Thanks to Emily, the jury saw Hajar as a real person. A person who had hopes of becoming a teacher one day. A sister and daughter desperately loved by her family. A houseproud, graceful woman. They saw just how she was treated by her monster of a husband, and he was found guilty of the murder of Hajar al-Mutairi and sentenced to life in prison, to serve a minimum of twenty-three years.

Detective Constable Emily Rogers served twenty-nine years in the Yorkshire Police Service. During her career she progressed to become the force-wide Family Liaison Coordinator in Major Crime, and worked in many different units, including the Vice Squad and Intelligence Unit. She received several force and judges' commendations, as well as a mention in Parliament for her contribution to murder investigations over a twenty-five-year period.

When asked to sum up her career, she said, *'Over the years it has been a privilege to seek justice for, and give a voice back to, the victims who have been killed. I have learned to never underestimate the impact of losing a loved one to murder.'*

Chapter 10

Domestic incidents are the bread and butter of policing across the country. Ask any officer what the most common emergency call is, and they'll tell you it's domestic arguments, abuse or family disputes.

They may be standard, but they should never be approached casually. A domestic call can range from the most common – an argument that has got loud and out of hand – to the most severe – a domestic murder. An officer worth their salt will try to keep people out of kitchens, due to the accessibility of knives. They'll make sure they're wearing their stab-proof vest, and they'll keep their eyes on escape routes. Add to that the high probability that there'll be children in the house, and domestic calls can be incredibly challenging to deal with, and many stay with the officers who deal with them for a long time.

Happy Valley successfully laces the reality of domestic abuse throughout its storylines without it ever becoming gratuitous. A pharmacist, a police officer, a PE teacher and an accountant, all outwardly respectable men, are exposed as abusive bullies – reflecting just how prolific domestic abuse is in all walks of society. Not only do police officers need to treat each domestic incident with the utmost diligence, they also need to have their wits about them. They have to *want* to find the truth in a situation, or have the nose to sniff it out – like fictional Sergeant Catherine Cawood does when she firsts meets Joanna Hepworth. Catherine knows that sometimes things aren't as they seem and immediately suspects Joanna's husband of abusing her. The fact that one of the Hepworths' daughters never feels safe enough to take her coat off, even when at home, makes her determined to get to the truth.

When children are involved in abuse or being neglected, it's hard to remain professional, as PC Lisa Groome, who we first met in Chapter Two, knows all too well.

Now

PC Lisa Groome releases her seat belt as the marked police car takes the last corner. She can see the address up ahead. She's been here before. She knows there's four kids in that house. She and her partner, Dan, had only been a couple of roads away, and already in the car, when the emergency call came in. *By the grace of God*, Lisa thinks now, as they approach the three-bed semi. She's glad they don't have to waste precious minutes searching for the address.

They'd both drawn breath when they'd heard the call.

'We've had a kiddie ring in saying, "Daddy's hanging in the garage." Emergency response required. Ambulance en route.'

It's a Saturday night in summer and it's only just turned dark. The short ride has been silent, focused. Dan's hands tight on the wheel, Lisa's mind on CPR techniques. As Dan pulls up to the address, Lisa looks past the house and towards the garage. She remembers the layout of the property now that she's here. The garage is set back from the house, at the end of a driveway that hugs the side of the property. It's an up-and-over door, and it's not been pulled all the way shut; a two-foot oblong of light shines out from the bottom.

Inside, a tiny bike lies on its side. It's bright pink. The type of bike a toddler would use. Next to the bike, about two inches from the floor, she can see the toes of a pair of trainers. As she focuses on the shoes, she sees them twitch, and she's out of the car and running towards the garage.

Four months earlier

Lisa sits in the section box, feet on the desk, eating chips from greasy paper. The 'box' is actually a tiny police station. A one-storey, brick-built rectangle, with a flat roof, one small window and two doors. You'd be forgiven for thinking it is a public toilet block, and the only thing that distinguishes it from the public loos is a paltry sign that sticks out at a right angle from the building, with 'Police' in blue chunky letters. The inside reminds her of the portable classrooms she used to have at school: thin, chipboard walls, painted in cream. The sign on Lisa's section box is wonky. She suspects someone has jumped up and slapped it, just to prove they could reach.

There's around eight or nine section boxes dotted around her local ward of Yorkshire. They were brought in as a force-wide initiative to promote 'community policing' after numerous complaints that residents never see police officers on the streets any more. Two to four officers are posted at each box and they are responsible for covering their area. Lisa likes working a local beat. It means she gets a regular partner, she's got to know the community that lives around her, and she knows the dynamics of the people who live here. But just because she is based in the community, it doesn't mean she is kissing babies and chatting to old ladies on street corners. She deals with anything that happens on her patch, from the mildest of neighbour disputes to the most violent of murders. Lisa knows the faces she needs to know, the places they like to hide and the first pawn shop to check after a burglary. Her partner is Dan, who has six years more service than she does and she trusts him with her life. He's married with kids and they often joke that Lisa spends more time with him than his actual wife. At the end of her career, Lisa will say that he was one of the best partners she ever had. A dry sense of humour, a local man, they could depend on each other when the shit hit the fan.

The thing that Lisa likes most about having a regular beat is it enables her to *cut the crap*. She considers herself part of a *nucleus* of police officers. She deals with people every day who try to pull the wool over her eyes, but they forget that she stopped them the week before with a pocket full of drugs and cash. They forget that you know them. She knows people by face, by their street names, knows what benefits they're on, who's sleeping with who and whose boyfriend is knocking them about. And sometimes, if she was lucky and told it like it is, she started to build a little respect.

Their beat is Neartown. A poor community, with lots of back-to-back housing, cheap rentals, houses of multiple occupancy and a diverse, multicultural population. There's a large Asian population, as well as an increasing number of Eastern European migrants, and the degradation is widespread.

Dan comes out of the toilet and sits down across the desk from her. He sighs contentedly as he unwraps his fish dinner, steam rolling upwards as he folds back the paper. He's about to take his first bite as their radios pipe up.

'We've got a domestic call on now to 83 Billet Way, a neighbour's rung to say they can hear screaming 'n' shouting coming from t'house. There's young'uns on the property.'

Dan groans in frustration and shoves a handful of chips into his mouth before rewrapping his dinner. Lisa picks up her radio.

'Foxtrot 61 – show us assigned.' She gives the control room their call sign and they head for the car. The address is only about two hundred yards away, on a street perpendicular to the one the section box is on, but they both know you don't waste seconds when attending a domestic. Many of the residents take pride in their houses and they pass neat front gardens, as well as the occasional shabby exterior, where the flowers are replaced with rotting furniture, old fridges and piles of rubbish. Lisa cranes her neck to look at the house numbers and points ahead and to the left.

'It'll be up there, on t'left.'

They park and get out of the car, strapping on their officer safety belts before approaching the house. You're supposed to wear the belts at all times, but the moulded car seats make the heavy equipment dig into your waist, making wearing them whilst travelling painful. Domestic calls are notorious for getting heated, and you don't want to go in there without your kit belt. The additional reassurance of your cuffs, baton and CS spray is always welcome when dealing with a situation that could go sideways at any moment. The house is quiet as they approach. Likely because the occupants have heard the sirens. Dan knocks on the door.

The woman who opens it is red in the face. Her hair, pulled back in a high bun, is escaping on either side, strands falling into her face. Her eyes are watery and a crying baby sits on her hip.

'You'd better come in.'

She leads them into a tidy sitting room. A man stands in one corner, arms crossed. He's breathing heavily, a sheen of sweat on his forehead. He's a lump of a man, at least six foot tall and heavy-set. The woman sits on one of the sofas and plops the baby down beside her. She's barely five foot tall and slim as a whippet. There are three other children in the room, the eldest looks around eight. Lisa looks at the woman and considers that she must have spent the last ten years of her life almost continually pregnant. No wonder she looks exhausted.

'Is this everyone, or are there more hiding under the stairs?' Dan keeps it light.

'This is all of us,' the woman answers. 'Baby Ruby, then Rory, three, Mary – she's six – and Connor is eight.' She points to the children at her feet.

'Could the kids go upstairs, d'you think?' Lisa makes the suggestion.

'Connor, lad, take the babies up.' This comes from Dad. The eldest boy gets up without a word and gathers his siblings, the four of them making their way carefully and obediently up the stairs.

Lisa waits until she hears the kids' voices fade and doors close.

'Someone's called us saying there's been shouting.'

'Fucking nosey bastards,' Dad mumbles. He's unsteady on his feet and the smell of alcohol lingers in the air.

'Come and have a chat with me, mate, in t'kitchen.' Dan walks towards the father, who, for a split second, looks like he may disagree, before his shoulders slump and he slopes towards the kitchen. Dan closes the door behind them.

'You okay, love? Mind if I sit?' The woman nods and Lisa takes the sofa opposite.

'What's been going on, then?'

'We've just been fighting, that's all. Just shouting, I mean, not fighting. Like, we haven't touched each other, nothing like that. It's just . . .'

'Just what, love?' Lisa leans in, encouraging the woman to talk to her. She doesn't know what the woman will say next, so braces herself for an allegation of the worst kind.

'It's just so hard.' The woman starts to cry.

Lisa moves to sit next to her, placing a hand gently on her back. 'That's it, love, let it out.'

The woman sobs and Lisa waits. Her gut wrenches in sympathy for the woman and she watches her, silently scoping for any visible injuries, or any sign of physical pain.

After a minute or two, Lisa says, 'I have to ask this, love. Has he hurt you?'

'No.' The woman shakes her head, her voice thick. Lisa reaches into the pocket of her stab vest and pulls out a packet of tissues. She hands one to the woman.

'What's your name?'

'Jill.' The woman sniffs.

'What's happened today, Jill?'

'I just lost it with him.' Jill straightens her back and blows her nose. 'He does fuck all. Absolutely fuck all! He lost his job about a month ago, but is he looking for a new one? Is he fuck. He sits around here all day, drinking. I wouldn't mind so much if he helped out with the kids, or tidied up once in a while, but no, he just sits on his arse and drinks all day. He must have changed three nappies in his life! I have to do everything. Everything! I go out to work, come back, and the kids aren't fed, the house is a wreck. He spends all I earn on his beer and then fucking moans at me when I don't want to shag him! Well, why the fuck would I?'

Lisa looks around the room. It's spotless. She looks at the cracked and dry skin on Jill's hands.

'He's not hurt me. I don't think he would. He's not a mean drunk, more like a sad one. He says he's depressed, ha! Join the fucking club, mate. It'd be nice to have time to be depressed! You've just got to get on wi' it, 'aven't you? I just can't stand it any more. He's feckless.'

Lisa takes some details down in her pocket book: the kids' names, dates of birth, where they go to school. It's all details that social services might want to know, should the need arise. Although Lisa wonders why she bothers; it's so rare that children's services have ever taken action on any of the reports she has submitted. Apparently, living in a home with domestic abuse is fine for the kids so long as no one is beating them. She tries not to think about the effect that it will be having on the little ones, listening to their parents rip each other to shreds every day. Once Jill has calmed down a bit, Lisa goes into the kitchen. Dan is drinking a cup of tea and points to one on the table.

'I made that for Jill, plenty of sugar.'

Lisa brings the cup to Jill and she takes it gratefully.

Luke, the husband, goes up to check on the kids, and Lisa and Dan discuss things in the kitchen.

'What did he say, then?'

'The usual.' Dan pulls a face. 'Says she's a nag, he's depressed, he's lost his job and feels like he can't provide for the family. Which makes him more depressed, which makes him drink, which makes her mad, and on and on.' He glances towards the sitting room. 'Has she made any allegations?'

'No.' Lisa sighs. 'I don't think he's knocking her about, just being a useless sod by the sounds of it. I think things got on top of them, that's all.'

'Lovely.' Dan gulps the rest of his tea. 'Let's wrap things up then, shall we. Maybe my dinner will still have a bit o' heat in it.'

Lisa smiles and they head back into the sitting room. Before they leave, and making sure that Luke is still out of earshot, Lisa gives Jill strict instructions to call 999 if she feels scared, if Luke hurts her or the kids, or if she needs help. She can tell by the look in Jill's eyes as she listens to the advice that she's unlikely to call. Some people will never think that calling the police is a viable option. Many think that things will only get worse if the police show up and more are just suspicious of authority. Jill thanks them for coming. On the way back to the car, Lisa asks Dan if he thinks social services will want to know about the family.

'With that amount of kids, they may already know about them.' He shakes his head. 'The house is clean, they're cared for. They've got toys, there's food in the fridge. Mum obviously looks after things well. They've just had a row, that's all. Got a bit loud. Same as hundreds of couples across the country. What's social services going to do with the information if you do send it in?'

'Yeah, you're probably right.' She'd like to send a report, but technically there is no requirement for her to do so. There'd been no crime alleged and, as Dan has pointed out, the kids are cared for. She thinks of some of the awful shitholes she's seen kids living in with no action from social services and decides that the report would just be marked as 'no concerns' anyway.

They get in the car. Dan guns the engine and licks his lips, and they head back to the station box to complete their paperwork. On the way, Lisa lets the control room know the result of the call.

'No crimes alleged, just an argument between husband and wife that got a bit loud, no injuries, no offences.'

'Thanks, Foxtrot 61.'

As they approach the section box Lisa wonders if Jill was hiding anything. She tries not to feel frustrated with the woman; she knows that it's hard to open up about domestic abuse, she knows many women are scared. But she can't help feeling like she's banging her head against a brick wall when women won't ask for help. She immediately feels guilty for thinking this and reminds herself that she mustn't become numb to the realities of the jobs she deals with. She may attend five domestic calls in a day, but for each victim, their emergency is the only thing that matters. In most cases, if police have been called, it's for something big. Each of them deserves her compassion.

Now

As Lisa runs towards the garage, eyes on the twitching feet, she remembers the second time they had attended this address. Jill had smashed a pot in frustration. Another row in front of the kids. The pink bike glares at her from the garage floor. *Where are the kids?*

She reaches the garage door, Dan a step behind her, and they lift it together. The loud scraping sound rattles her teeth as she leaps towards Luke's jerking body. She's seen that jerking before. *The death dance.* It's the body's last fight to stay alive. They have seconds to save Luke's life. Less than seconds. Without words, they know what each of them will do. There's no communication required when you work with someone day in, day out. Dan will take the weight. Lisa will cut the cord. Dan grabs Luke around the thighs and lifts him as Lisa grabs for his neck. Screams erupt around her. Or has there always been screaming? She realizes that all four children are in the garage with them.

'Go back into the house!' Lisa shouts, keeping her focus on Luke's neck. The kids huddle together, the eldest holding the baby, but they don't leave. She glances quickly at them, sees the look of hope in their faces, their hope in her.

The police are here to save the day. To save Daddy.

She doesn't have time to think about what will happen if she can't. She doesn't have time to comfort them. To stop them seeing this. She snaps her attention back to the ligature around Luke's neck. Washing line. The type that's plastic-coated nylon. The knot has pulled so tight with the weight of his body that it's tiny. She'll never be able to untie it. She looks to Dan. He has a Leatherman utility knife in his kit belt. Technically, as per the rest of the population of the UK, police aren't supposed to carry knives. For a start, knives that are anything larger than your standard Swiss army are usually defined as offensive weapons, plus, it could get sticky explaining in court why a police officer stabbed someone in self-defence. But this situation is exactly why some do. One look at Dan's face reminds her that their belts are in the car.

Fuck.

Luke has stopped twitching. His face is red and his lips are deepening in colour from purple to dark blue. His eyes bulge. She hasn't got time to get back to the car. If she leaves him hanging from this garage roof, he will die. The washing line has cut so deep into his neck that she can barely see it, so she looks to the knot that attaches to the metal strut on the roof. Not for the first time in her life, she thanks God that she's six foot tall. She starts to pull at the knot that is attaching Luke to the roof. *I can't do this, it won't undo, this is impossible.* She ignores the thoughts in her mind and keeps going, because she's got no other choice. If she stops, he will die. *Those children will watch their father die.* Incredibly, the knot begins to loosen. She works at it, her fingers aching with the effort, her nails tearing, and finally, after what seems like hours, the knot comes free.

Luke drops like a dead weight into Dan, and they both

fall to the floor. Lisa runs. Back to the car, into the front seat, grabbing the kit belts. There's no way they'll be able to get that cord from around his neck without a knife. As she sprints back to the garage, she hears sirens in the distance. *Please God, let that be the ambulance.* She kneels next to Luke, who's now completely unresponsive. With Dan's help, they get their fingers under the tight band of cord around his neck, and she is able to push the blade beneath the washing line and cut it free. The sirens are right outside now and the paramedics are in and starting CPR before Dan or Lisa have the time to start it themselves.

Lisa is panting with exertion and adrenaline. Each time she has to fight to save someone's life, it hits her the same. All she wants to do is sit back on the garage floor and press her sore fingertips onto the cool concrete. She knows that later, when she tries to sleep, she will see Luke's purple face floating before her eyes. It will join the ones she's tried to save before. The ones she couldn't help. But there's no time to rest. She pulls herself up and walks towards the children, who are still screaming. She peers out of the garage, door now fully open, and sees neighbours lining the street. She gathers the wet-faced children, picks up the toddler, ushering them through to the inside of the house.

'Where's Mum?' she asks the eldest, Connor.

'She's left us. She don't live here no more.' He shrugs.

'What d'you mean she don't live here any more?'

'She left us. Ages ago.'

'Is Daddy going to be okay?' the small girl, Mary, asks Lisa.

'Daddy's being looked after, don't worry,' Lisa says, turning back to Connor. 'Have you got Mum's number?'

Connor shakes his head then looks to the door of the garage, behind her. She turns to see her duty inspector walk in.

'Lisa, you're to go up hospital with the fella, they're still working on him and we need someone to provide continuity if he does—' He stops himself, glancing at the small faces gathered around her. 'Well, off you go, they're loading him on t'ambulance as we speak. Apparently, Mum's on the way, one of the neighbours has called her.'

Lisa nods, turns back to the children. 'Did you hear that? Mummy's on the way.'

Pale faces and wide eyes follow her as she walks away. She wants to scoop them up and take them straight to their mother. She wants to stay and make sure they're okay. She wants to hug them until they feel safe, but she can't do any of those things, so she grits her teeth and heads to the waiting ambulance.

Two months later

Lisa sits in a large police van as streams of football fans wave past her. Chants fill the air and the smell of beer and sweat washes into the vehicle on the breeze. The fans are, thankfully, in good spirits. She takes a moment to rest her eyes, leaning back in the seat and rolling her shoulders. They ache from wearing her body armour all day.

Someone clears their throat nearby and her eyes snap open.

'It's you, i'n't it?'

She recognizes the man standing in front of her immediately. He's smiling uncertainly, pulling at the football scarf that is wrapped closely about his throat. A flashback to his face, swollen and purple, back in the garage with that pink bike.

'I just wanted to say thank you for what you did that night – I mean it, I would've died if it weren't for you.' He leans in towards her, raising his voice so that he can be heard over the noise of the football fans. She smells beer on his breath. It takes her a second or two to respond, reeling a little from him appearing in front of her, her mind going again to that damn pink bike and wondering how anyone could think to use their own child's toy to try to top themselves.

She shakes her head. 'No worries.'

'No,' he says, shaking his own head, 'I mean it. Not many would've kept trying like you did. I realized as soon as I'd done it – fucking idiot.' He looks at the floor, swaying slightly. 'Anyway, I've sorted m'self out, like, that was my rock bottom. But, because of you, and your mate, I'm alright. I'm doing alright.'

'Honestly,' she says, feeling sympathy wash over her, 'it's my job. I'm glad you made it.'

He nods at the floor, then to her. Lifts a hand and shuffles away.

As she watches him go, she considers how lucky he was. Does he know how close he came to succeeding? If Lisa and her partner hadn't been in their car, yards away from the house, when the call came in. If the paramedics hadn't arrived when they did. If his son hadn't found him and dialled 999. If it weren't for every moment of that emergency call going right, he wouldn't be merrily shambling away from her police van right now. Lisa doesn't believe in God, but something, somewhere, had decided it wasn't his time that night last summer.

The following summer

'We've got a call.' Dan walks in to the section box and lobs Lisa's hat across the room. She catches it in one hand, wise to his friendly attempts to catch her out. It's the beginning of a Sunday night shift, the warmth of the day has disappeared, and she shivers as she follows him out to the car.

'What we got?'

Dan turns to her and grimaces. 'Reports of four kids home alone. Down Billet Way.'

She frowns at him, her brain connecting dots.

'Four kids.' Dan raises an eyebrow.

'Not the same address, though?' She looks at him. 'Can't be, can it?'

'How many families have four kids?' he asks, adding, 'It's literally about ten houses away from where we were before.'

'We'd better get moving.' She climbs into their police car

and Dan drives towards the row of semis they'd attended the previous summer.

On the way to the address Lisa wonders if it's the same family. Have they moved? Luke had said he'd sorted himself out. She'd hoped it was true.

She recognizes Connor as he timidly opens the door and her heart sinks. He hasn't grown. The front door opens directly into a small sitting room and as she steps in, she sees that with the exception of the baby, none of them seem to have got any bigger than they were last year. The cheeks that were previously round are now hollow. The clothes that were clean are now dirty and ill-fitting. The place is sparse, just a large television sitting on a small table, and one sofa. A few boxes strewn around the room. It looks as if they moved in yesterday. There're no personal touches, no photos, no cushions – the carpet is stained and threadbare.

Connor walks to the sofa and curls in next to the two siblings already there. The baby, maybe one and a half now, just in a nappy, lies on the floor on a grubby-looking blanket. She can see that the nappy is heavy with urine. The three older children huddle together as Lisa talks to them.

'Don't worry, you're not in any trouble. You've met me before, everything's okay.'

Rory, who must be six now, slips down onto the floor and holds the baby's hands as it starts to grizzle. Only Connor meets Lisa's eyes.

'We remember.'

'Okay, right.' Lisa keeps her voice low and calm. 'Who do you live with?'

'Daddy.'

'Where's Mummy?'

'Don't know. She doesn't live with us.'

Lisa glances around the room again, remembering the woman's touches at their previous home. There are none of those here. The room feels cold, and hard; Lisa glances at the barely clothed baby, separated from the gross carpet only by the thin material of its blanket. The children in front of her are filthy. She tries not to flinch as Mary, the second eldest, scratches her head, lice jumping on her hand. She thinks of the Victorian beggar children that are portrayed in old films like *Oliver Twist* and can't believe that these children are sitting in front of her in the twenty-first century. She regularly sees neglected children, but she can't remember seeing anything this disturbing for a long time.

She notices that Rory is chewing on something.

'What've you got there, love?'

He holds out his hand, opening his fingers to reveal half a raw sausage. Lisa swallows the urge to vomit.

'Where'd you get that from?'

'Fridge.'

She takes a look around the small kitchen. Dirty plates are piled in the sink and empty beer cans and alcohol bottles litter the surfaces. The fridge is empty, save for half a pack of raw sausages, the packaging torn away at one side. She searches the rest of the house and discovers no baby food and no nappies.

'When did you last eat?' she asks, as she comes back into the sitting room. Dan is kneeling on the floor, picking up the baby. He wraps it as best he can in the blanket.

Connor shrugs. The rest continue to stare at her as she moves around the room, following her with their wide eyes.

'Do you know where Daddy is?'

'He's in the pub.'

'Do we know which pub he's in?'

'No.' Connor jumps up and runs out of the room. Lisa wonders if she's upset him, before he runs back in with a crumpled piece of paper in his hands. There's a telephone number scrawled across it.

'We've to ring this number for Daddy's pub.'

Lisa takes the paper and walks to the house phone that's sitting on the floor in the corner of the room. She dials the number, clenching her jaw as it rings. She is looking at the small boy who was eating raw meat. He's now finished, and licking the palm of his grubby hand.

The landlord answers, and Lisa asks if Luke is there.

'Oh, erm – no, love, no. I mean, he does come in 'ere but, er – not tonight, not seen him.'

Lisa grits her teeth. 'Well, maybe you can pass him a message – if he *happens* to turn up – it's PC Groome from Yorkshire Police and I'm taking his kids into protective custody, so he'd better get his arse up to t'police station.'

'Oh – I, hang on . . .' Lisa can hear muffled voices, imagines the landlord's fat fingers over the receiver. She hasn't got time for this. She hangs up, turning to face the kids.

'Right, you lot, we're going on a little trip.'

Dan and Lisa gather what they can from the house – half a pack of baby wipes, a couple of sad-looking soft toys and an empty changing bag. They look for clean clothes to bring for the kids and manage to find a small selection, buried under piles of dirty laundry in an upstairs bedroom. The only thing they can find to carry it all in is a large plastic shopping bag. They stuff everything in and head for the car.

Once back at the nick, the challenge of juggling the kids whilst also completing all the paperwork required for an emergency child protection order begins. The various reports needed mean that you often have to write things out in triplicate. Usually this drives Lisa up the wall – why she can't write one report and photocopy it for anyone else who needs to see it is beyond her – but in cases of child neglect, she gets why it's so important. There can be nothing missed or overlooked in cases like this.

They take the children into the front office, where the station officer, Rose, has a wide smile for them, and reaches for baby Ruby. Dan eagerly hands her over and goes to find the duty inspector, who needs to be briefed whenever children are taken into protective custody.

As the children surround Rose, who has reached into a stationery drawer and is pulling out bright-coloured highlighters and sheets of paper, Lisa motions to her over the kids' heads.

'Nits,' she mouths, pointing down at the children's hair.

Rose shrugs, smiling. She leans in closer to the children and Lisa resists the urge to scratch her head. She's been itching all over since they left the house. She tells herself that it's all in her mind and concentrates on what needs doing next. Calling social services. She pulls out her pocket book and is looking through the useful numbers scrawled at the back when a colleague pops their head into the office.

'There's a buffet in canteen.' She nods at the kids. 'Left over from some party earlier for the top brass. They've got sausage rolls.'

'Sausage rolls!' the three-year-old, Rory, exclaims.

Lisa nods – priorities – *let's get these starving children fed*.

They walk into the canteen and the kids run at the table in the centre, where the leftover buffet food is spread out. Sandwiches, sausage rolls, sausages on sticks, crisps, cheese, and more. It's all slightly curled at the edges but the kids don't care. Before Lisa can react, Mary has stuffed five cubes of cheese in her mouth. Rory is mainlining cocktail sausages.

'You'll turn into a sausage, you,' Lisa says with a smile.

He giggles, and suddenly they're all laughing. Laughing and stuffing and chewing.

'Careful, kids,' Lisa warns lightly, 'chew it properly, take your time, it's not going anywhere.' She's worried what the sudden influx of food will do to empty stomachs, but she hasn't got the heart to stop them.

She walks to the phone in the corner of the canteen and dials 9 for an outside line, before stabbing in the number for the emergency social services.

The duty social worker picks up after twelve long rings and Lisa wonders whether they were having a nap. She explains the situation and hears the social worker's voice drop.

'Four? It's going to be difficult to place four.'

'I'm sure you'll manage.' Lisa fights to keep the frustration out of her voice. She instantly gets the impression that the social worker is annoyed at the task of making these children safe. Not for the first time when talking to children's services, Lisa asks herself why people can't just do their job properly and with at least a pretence at enthusiasm. She holds back from telling the social worker she should be happy that these kids have been taken to a place of safety, not disgruntled.

The social worker is aware of the family. She'll have to do some ringing around. Lisa gives her the number of the station office to call back on. She puts the phone down and looks at the kids: three of them are still eating, Connor is passing the smaller ones what they want, and Rory has put his head on the table and fallen asleep. Lisa is about to nudge him awake when Rose walks in.

'Dad's in the front office.' She raises an eyebrow. 'He's not happy.'

Lisa marches for the door. 'Can you watch these?' Rose nods as Lisa passes her, muttering, 'He's going to be even more unhappy in a minute.'

Lisa walks into the public waiting area of the station's front office to see Luke standing at the counter, banging his fist and shouting. He sees her and turns to face her. She winces at the smell of booze on his breath as he shouts, 'What have you done with my kids? How dare you take my kids!'

'Oi!' Lisa shouts, louder than him, so that he understands exactly what kind of mood she's in. He shuts his mouth. 'Do you remember who I am?'

He nods. Looks at the floor.

'Right.' She stands in front of him, lowering her voice. She does not soften it. 'You just sit down there and keep your gob shut.' She points to one of the plastic waiting-room chairs. 'Your kids – you're a disgrace of a father! They've all got head lice. They're starving.' She realizes that her voice is rising and she's jabbing a finger at his chest with every point she makes, but she doesn't care. She's so angry. 'You've got no nappies for your baby, who's not been changed all day. They're half-dressed, crawling with nits. You're going to sit there, you're going to wait and you're going to keep that gob firmly shut.' He lowers himself into the chair and she begins to walk away. Just as she gets to the door that takes her back into the station office, she stops. She turns back to him, heart pounding in her chest. 'You – you don't deserve to breathe God's clean air.'

He shrinks into the chair and she buzzes herself back through. Rose has returned with the kids and is sitting them in one of the front-office interview rooms. Rory curls up on a chair and closes his eyes again.

Lisa looks to Rose and points back to Luke. 'He moves, makes a fuss, makes a *sound*. Shout me.'

Rose nods.

The phone in the office rings and it's social services.

'Okay, have you located Dad?'

'Yeah, he's in front office,' Lisa says. 'He's very drunk.'

'Well – as I said before – it's really difficult to place four kids, we may have to consider letting Dad take them home, and then we can pick this up in the week.'

'Right.' Lisa closes her eyes and takes a deep breath, fearing that if she doesn't, she will say something she regrets. She expects to wade through a load of shit when dealing with the public, but not when she's talking to agencies that are supposed to be partners with policing. 'What's your name?'

'Sorry?'

'What's your name?'

'What d'you need my name for?'

'I want your name, so that when we've got four little bodies to bury, I know who to blame.'

'Now – that's a bit much.'

'Is it? These kids are malnourished, they've been on their own all day, eating raw sausages, they're filthy, they're covered in head lice – what more needs to happen to them before you'll do something? He is drunk. He's been drinking all day. I cannot give those children back to that man. It might be that they go back to him eventually, but not tonight. I won't do it.'

'Right – well – I'll have to speak to my supervisor about this.'

'You do that.'

'I'll call you back.'

'No – you won't. I'll hold. I'm not putting this phone down till you tell me this is sorted.'

The social worker huffs. Hold music fills the line. Lisa rests her head in her hands and closes her eyes. It could be minutes or hours later when the social worker comes back on the line and Lisa jerks her head up.

'We'll have to split them up. Girls and boys.'

'That's fine. So long as none of them are alone – that's fine.' She can cope with the idea that they will be split up, but none of them must be alone. Having to split siblings up after incidents like these is heartbreaking, and she doesn't think she could take the screaming if one was taken from the others by themselves. It's a screaming she's heard before.

Lisa gets the addresses of the foster houses and colleagues are assigned to drop off Rory and Connor. As the police car ferrying the boys to their home for a night leaves the yard, the boys wave goodbye to their sisters, who are already crying for their brothers. Lisa and Dan load the girls into their car for the second time that night and head towards the foster address. Dan is holding the baby, still wrapped in the paltry blanket. Lisa has been to the foster home before, she's happy that the girls are being placed with such a nice couple. She's glad that she can take them there, pass over her responsibility in person. The couple are older, and have three beautiful bedrooms permanently made up for emergency placements. Lisa watches as Mary marvels at their bedroom for the night, as she runs her grubby fingers over the clean, soft bedding and reverently touches the lined-up dolls. She wonders if Mary remembers the time before her mum left. If she remembers the time she had clean clothes and soft things. She wonders where their mother is. Has she remarried? Does she have more children?

A bath is running as Lisa and Dan leave. Lisa wants to see them clean. She wants to see them clean and sleepy and dressed in pretty pyjamas. But her job is done. They're safe now.

By the time Lisa gets back to the station to start the paper-work, Luke is in a cell. He's been arrested on suspicion of child neglect. Lisa wonders how he got to the point where drink is more important than his own children, and how many more cases like this she can cope with before her sanity abandons her.

Lisa never had dealings with the family again. She often thinks about those children, where they are and what they're doing now. Whether they remember their father hanging in the garage, whether they followed in his foot-steps. Whether they have children of their own. She hopes that they broke the cycle of neglect and abuse.

Tiny toddler bikes, especially pink ones, still send her back to that night in the garage.

PC Lisa Groome served thirty years in policing. She pro-gressed upwards to the rank of Chief Inspector, and worked in many different units, including response policing,

neighbourhood policing, investigation and firearms com-
manding. Lisa would like to highlight that the way police
forces respond to reports of domestic abuse has changed
significantly for the better since this incident occurred.
Legislation has also been implemented to protect victims
and give the police more powers to protect those who are
subjected to domestic abuse. When asked to sum up her
career, she said, '*It was an incredible roller coaster of highs
and lows. One day you're walking into training school as a
shiny bright new bobby, then suddenly you blink, and it's
time to hang up your helmet and handcuffs. I've seen so
many changes, from wearing skirts and carrying handbags,
to full body armour! What sits below all the changes in the
last thirty years is the internal drive to serve the public and
to protect those who need you in a time of crisis. When you
do help that person, it's a feeling you can't describe and it
stays with you for ever. Policing is for ever in my heart and
soul – you're always a bobby.*'

Chapter 11

Each time a police officer leaves the safety of their police station they face the threat of being seriously hurt, or killed, on duty. Thankfully, in the UK, officers are rarely killed in the line of duty, but it does happen, and sadly many are physically assaulted on a daily basis. According to statistics published on the GOV.UK website, there were almost 37,000 assaults on UK police officers in 2020–2021, of which just over 11,000 resulted in injury.*

These assaults range from being pushed, punched or

* 'Annex: Statistics on the number of police officers assaulted in the year ending March 2021, England and Wales' – GOV.UK (www.gov.uk)

spat at, to the more serious attacks that lead to broken bones and changed lives. There is not a police officer out there, serving today, that does not consider the risk of death or serious injury regularly. Nonetheless, they continue to put on their uniform, step out of the station and walk towards the danger. Sergeant Catherine Cawood, *Happy Valley*'s unchallenged and unthwartable fictional hero, receives a number of injuries throughout the three series of the show, mostly from her nemesis, Tommy Lee Royce. Each time she gets thrown down, she climbs her way back onto her feet – nothing will stop her from getting out there and protecting the public.

Though *Happy Valley* lays the violence on thick, there are real policewomen out there who have been injured just as seriously as our Catherine. Some criminals, those with a deep hatred of the police, don't see a woman when a female police officer approaches them. They just see a uniform. Policewomen, therefore, are just as vulnerable as policemen when it comes to the chances of being attacked on duty. Some claim that women are *more* vulnerable to attack than their male counterparts. But one thing I am one hundred per cent confident of – women are just as capable as men of being highly trained in officer safety manoeuvres. They're just as capable of saving themselves and their colleagues when faced with dangerous offenders, as PC Penelope Curtis proved during a vicious attack on duty.

'If you had to get nicked for something, what would the offence be?'

Police Constable Penelope Curtis looks across at her operator, who is eagerly waiting for an answer to his question. Mo has been in the police for two months, and still has the bright wide eyes of a puppy that's just been given a new ball.

'The serial murder of over-excited probationers,' Penny answers, returning her eyes to the road.

'Oh, come on.' Mo laughs. 'I mean, what would your most likely offence be? Like, what crime are you most likely to commit?'

'You do ask some stupid questions.' Penny slows the marked police vehicle she's driving, so that she can get a better look at the man on the pavement. They are patrolling their local patch during a merciful break from emergency calls, and the man has caught her eye.

'I've been a police officer for nearly twenty years, I'm not *likely* to be committing anything.'

'I asked Matty, and he said—'

'Shut up.' Penny cuts across him, pointing a thumb towards the rear windscreen. 'That man we just passed; he's wanted.'

'Who?' Mo begins to twist in his seat, looking backwards. 'The one who was talking to himself?'

'Yeah, he's schizophrenic. I'm turning round – don't think he clocked us.' Penny swings into the driveway of a nearby house and turns the vehicle around. 'Nick Brooks. He's frequently off his head and he hates us, so get ready for a fight. Saw him on the briefing a couple days ago – wanted for failing to appear.'

'I see him – blue coat, red hair?'

'That's the one,' Penny confirms. 'Honestly, I don't know why courts give letters to people as mentally unwell as he is. Do they think he's going to read it? Put it in his diary – turn up in court on time?' She shakes her head. 'We'll need a van, on the hurry-up.'

'Control, from 5981,' Mo speaks into his radio.

'Go ahead, 5981.'

'We've sighted wanted male, Nick Brooks, on Smythe Avenue. Can we get a prisoner van to our location, junction Apex Road? On the hurry-up, please.'

'Received, 5981. Do you need more units?'

Mo looks to Penny, who shakes her head.

'Just the van for now, please,' he confirms.

Penny can see Brooks up ahead of them, walking with his head down. He's holding a plastic bag. 'He was fiddling in that bag when we drove past,' she says, unclipping her seat belt. 'Get it off him. It's probably just full of cider, but you never know.'

Mo nods, taking off his own seat belt and readying his hand on the door handle.

'Wait till he clears the houses, when he's walking next to the fence,' Penny instructs. 'It'll give him less ways to run.'

Penny waits until Brooks begins walking next to a long, high fence, then pulls the car to the kerb just ahead of him, so that he's now walking towards them. He doesn't lift his gaze from the pavement. He's not a tall man, standing the same height as Penny at 5'10, but he's got a thick build. A large head and a fat neck. She climbs out and blocks the

pavement, facing him, hands on her hips and feet wide. Mo
has jumped out of his side and jogs round the car, until he's
next to Brooks, who is still doing his best to ignore them.

'Nick!' Mo says.

'Nope,' Nick says, continuing to walk towards Penny.

'Hello, Mr Brooks,' she says, and he raises his face to
hers. Realizing that he's boxed in, with Penny in front and
Mo to his side, he stops.

'Fuck's sake,' he shouts, 'I've just come out for a drink.'

Now that they're close, Penny can hear the clinking of
glass. She can see the outline of what looks like three bottles of beer in the bag; its plastic is thin and stretched. She
can also smell cannabis, or more likely, skunk.

'You're wanted for failing to appear,' Mo says. 'You'll
need to come with us.'

'Am I fuck!' Brooks shouts, his eyes rolling unnervingly
in his heads. 'I'm not spending whole weekend in nick!'

It's a Friday evening. If Penny arrests Brooks now, he'll
have to stay in a cell until court opens on Monday. She
has sympathy for people who are unwell, but when they're
off their meds and smoking cannabis, she finds it hard to
be understanding. 'Listen, Nick, we've got a van on the
way. This is happening whether you like it or not, so why
don't you just put down the bag and we can do it the easy
way.'

'You get in the van, you die,' he mutters, talking to the
floor and shaking his head. Penny has the feeling that he's
not talking to her or Mo. She jerks her head at Mo, then to
the bag. *Get it off him.*

Mo lunges for the bag, but Nick is surprisingly quick – he swings the arm that's holding the bag until the plastic twists up and around his fist, then rotates his wrist quickly, winding the plastic tight, so that his fist is now lined with glass. Nick continues to talk to himself, his eyes flitting from Mo, to Penny, to the sky and back again. She catches some of what he's saying – *don't get in the van, don't trust them, fucking coppers* – but a lot of it is nonsensical.

Penny is in front of him, and Mo is to the side. He's blocked in on the other side by the fence. Both officers are standing in the ready position, feet wide, hands out to the side. Penny considers pulling her CS gas – a tear gas carried by all UK police officers – from its holster, but CS sometimes doesn't hit drugged-up people the same way it hits others. Sometimes it makes it worse. She pulls her baton instead, and is relieved to see Mo doing the same. Not for the first time, she wishes that 'care in the community' actually existed, and that the police weren't left to deal with mentally unstable people, who should have the right to be dealt with by mental health professionals. She hears the sound of sirens in the air and hopes it's the van speeding towards them.

'We'll wait for the others,' she says from the side of her mouth, low, to Mo, whose head bobs like a puppet that's lost its string. If she waits for more officers, it'll be safer to take Nick into custody. All they have to do is contain him until back-up gets here.

Her plan is short-lived. Nick suddenly stops muttering and starts shouting, 'More of them are coming, they're going to kill you!' In one quick move, he smashes his fist against the fence. He screams as the glass breaks across his hand, and then lunges at Mo, glass fist first.

Mo side-steps, ducking down and bringing his baton across Nick's shins, causing Nick to tip forward onto the floor. Penny is on him in a flash, pulling his arms behind his back. She places a cuff on his free hand, whilst Mo holds the glass fist up in the air. She can see blood beginning to seep from the plastic. She carefully unravels the bag and pulls it off Nick's hand, revealing deep lacerations in his palm. She places a cuff around his other hand, then stands and runs to the car for the first-aid kit.

The van pulls up behind her car and two of her colleagues jump out.

'All okay?' the driver, Matty, asks.

'It is now,' she replies, 'you missed all the action – as usual.'

'Fuck off.' He smiles, helping her with the first-aid kit.

They return to Nick and Mo. Nick is still on his front, his breathing laboured between sobs.

'Get him on his side,' she tells Mo, and he and Matty haul him into a position that will allow Nick to catch his breath.

'It's okay, Nick,' Penny says. 'I'm just going to bandage up your hand.'

'I've called an ambulance,' Mo tells her.

'You hear that, Nick?' Penny says, as she kneels before Nick's hands, still cuffed behind his back. 'You're going to get looked after soon.'

She presses a thick gauze pad into Nick's palm and wraps his fingers around it, winding the stretchy bandage around his balled fist.

'I never got to tell you what Matty chose as his crime,' Mo says, trying to wipe the dried blood from his hands with an ineffective wipe a paramedic gave him.

'I genuinely don't want to know,' Penny tells him, and walks to the back of the ambulance.

Nick is strapped onto the bed in the back. One of the paramedics has dealt with him before and managed to calm him down enough to let them treat his hand. He'll need stitches. Penny doesn't envy the doctor who'll have to do that.

Mo passes her and climbs in. As Nick is in police custody, they'll have to stay with him whilst he's being treated. Nick looks suspiciously at Mo, but the paramedic distracts him before he can react. Penny nods to her, impressed.

'I'll follow in the car,' she says to Mo, 'grab us a coffee on the way.'

He nods enthusiastically.

As she turns from the ambulance, Nick's voice makes her stop.

'I know who you are.'

She turns back, seeing that Nick is now straining against the straps of the trolley. He's looking at her, a manic expression in his eyes. 'I'm not stupid,' he says quietly. 'Do you think I am?'

Penny resists the urge to remind him that he's just sliced

his own hand up on beer bottles. Instead, she turns to Mo and winks. 'Enjoy your trip.'

She turns from them all and heads to her car, grateful that she's not the one having to sit in the back with Nick, but also feeling sorry for Mo. At twenty-four and newly married, he's still just a kid. Maybe she'll get him a muffin to go with his coffee.

The next day, Penny is in the PCs' writing room finishing up some crime reports. Mo is sitting beside her, on the neighbouring computer. They'd spent six hours at the hospital with Nick, before they could take him into custody and bed him down until Monday.

She opens up the Police National Computer database and brings up his criminal history. He has numerous convictions for possession of cannabis, public order offences and assaults. First conviction at age seventeen. Two assaults on police. He has warning signals – markers added to a person's record to warn the officers who may be dealing with them – of Mental, Suicidal, Weapons, Drugs. Mental stands for 'mental health issues' and she's always thought it sounds harsh shortened in that way.

'What a life,' she mutters.

'Who's that?'

'Our friend, Mr Brooks.'

She fills Mo in on some of what's on the screen.

'He gets diagnosed with schizophrenia in his late teens, when he starts getting in trouble with us lot.' She's read many of the crime reports he's been involved with, trying to get a picture of his life. She doesn't know why, but his words had stuck in her mind. *I know who you are.* She doesn't think she's ever met him before yesterday, although she can't be sure. Shouting, violent men all start to look the same once you've dealt with enough of them. 'He's frequently sectioned, but never seems to spend any real amount of time in mental hospitals. He seems to be stuck in a cycle of getting treatment, leaving treatment, going off his meds, smoking weed and then kicking off.'

'He needs taking off the streets,' Mo says, typing furiously. He's got five crime reports to write and only forty minutes before their shift is over. He wants to get home to his wife.

'He obviously can't be trusted to take his meds. It's always the same story, they'll wait until he really hurts someone – or worse – before he gets taken off the streets.'

Mo doesn't reply, and Penny realizes she's lost him to the pressure of finishing his reports. He's got a new wife at home and a baby on the way. No wonder he can't wait to finish his shift. She leaves him to it, standing up and heading to the yard for a cigarette.

As she exhales into the evening air, surrounded by the liveried vehicles of Yorkshire Police, she thinks about the dream she had last night. It's rare that the job interrupts her sleep. Up until now, eighteen years into service, she's been excellent at compartmentalizing. The jobs she deals with – the people – they stay at the nick. She leaves them behind, shakes them off, like her cuffs and kit belt, when she leaves each day. She flicks ash to the ground, leaning against the back of the prisoner van.

She knows that it's the randomness that has got to her. Violent schizophrenics have no motive. No reason. People can't protect themselves from them, because no one knows when they're going to have a violent episode, or where. The public can't avoid them, because they are allowed to live amongst us. They should be, of course. She'd never advocate for all schizophrenics to be locked away in institutions like the old days. She thinks back to a case where a man decapitated an 82-year-old woman during a mental episode. The case had terrified her. She'd asked herself at the time, *what would I have done?* She'd like to think she'd have put herself between him and the woman, but there's always a part of her, right at the back of her mind, that says, *I would freeze.*

She takes a long drag, trying to shake the incident from her head, and instead remembers waking up in a cold sweat last night. She'd been shouting when she woke, she was sure. Good thing she lives alone. Her throat was dry and she'd reached for the water she always has by her bed. Nick Brooks had been in her dream. He'd been standing in her garden. He was looking up at her, staring into her bedroom windows. His eyes were huge and glassy, spinning in his head. For some reason, she had woken up absolutely petrified.

She stubs the cigarette out on the side of a wall and

throws it into the large industrial bin in the yard. Better get back to it.

It's nearly a year later. Penny is once again posted with Mo, who's less like a puppy now and more like an adult springer spaniel – faster and more alert, but still with the potential for hyperactive silliness.

They're driving through the city centre when a call comes out over the radio.

'Immediate grade call now to a loud disturbance – neighbours have called stating that someone is screaming – sounds of a fight heard.'

Penny nods to Mo and flicks on her lights and sirens.

Mo assigns them to the call and Penny drives towards the north, taking the fastest route out of the city and towards the suburbs. She knows the street, wonders why it sounds familiar to her.

'Any intel?' she asks Mo.

It's his job, as her partner and the passenger, to update her on any information they have before they get to the call.

'Looks like it's a well-known address, standby.' He's scanning the screen in the centre of the dashboard.

'I definitely recognize it,' she confirms, keeping her eyes on the road as the traffic parts before her.

'Police have been here loads,' Mo says. 'Looks like it's a bit of a doss-house, lots of drinkers living here by the looks of it, lots of fights. There're plenty of names associated with it but no official residents that I can see.'

'Okay,' she says, racing towards the address. 'So, we're going in blind. Expect anything.'

'Expect anything,' he repeats to himself, and Penny hears it like a mantra.

Be ready.

There's a woman standing outside the house, waving her arms.

Penny looks at the address and knows she's been here before. She remembers a fight involving street drinkers, but not much else. They climb out of the car and the woman starts shouting at them.

'He's got Ted and the kid in there, he's going mental!' Penny recognizes the woman as one of the drinkers who hangs about in the park up the road. Her teeth are yellow and her hair is grey, she's only got one shoe on. Penny notices a cut above her eye.

'Are you hurt?'

'Don't worry about me – a scratch! It's Ted and the kid you need to worry about, he's going to kill them. It's the upstairs flat, on the left.'

'Kid? Is there a child in there?' Penny draws her baton.

'No, well, not really a kid – we just call him that,' the woman says. 'He's probably, like – eighteen, maybe?'

'Who's attacking them? Who's in there?' Mo shouts at her, snapping her attention to him.

'Fuck knows, never seen him before,' she says, pointing a shaking hand at the front door. 'Ted just turned up with him, seemed a nice bloke, then he just snapped, starts punching us.'

'Has he got any weapons?' Penny asks.

'No, I don't think so.'

Mo pulls his baton and they march towards the house. Now that the female informant has stopped screeching, they can hear their surroundings.

'Control, from 1972.' Penny talks low into her radio as they approach the front of the address. There's two front doors, so close together they look almost comical, like one was stuck on as an afterthought. The door on the left is wide open. The house is silent.

'G'head, Pen.'

'We'll need another unit at this address, please, possible injured people inside, male going nuts, no weapons seen – can we get an ambo running too.'

'Ambo – yes. Back-up – I've got no one up this end, I'll see if there's any over west I can send.'

'Received,' Penny says, cursing to herself. Back-up is at least twenty minutes away.

'We're on our own, then,' says Mo, as he peers into the hallway. It's long and narrow, with stairs at the end that lead up to the first-floor flat.

A flash of red catches Penny's eye and she points at it with her baton.

'Blood,' Mo says, his eyes following hers, to a bright-red streak on the hallway wall.

'Looks fresh, and it's too much to have come from her.'

Penny jerks a thumb at the woman they've left by the side of the road.

'Should we wait for back-up?'

Penny considers. She'd like to. Of course she would. The thought of climbing the dark, narrow stairs at the end of the corridor with only Mo and two batons was a frightening prospect.

'She said there's a kid in danger in there and I don't trust her estimation of his age one bit, being that she's a full-time pisshead. He could be young.'

'Right.' Mo nods, gripping his baton and gritting his teeth.

'Run and get the shield and first-aid kit from the boot, quick as you like.'

He's back in a matter of seconds. Penny takes the shield and holds it over her left shoulder. A loud thud sounds from the flat above them, followed by a faint groan. It sounds like someone is hurt. Penny's stomach drops at the noise, but her boots propel her forward, towards the stairs, the sound of someone in pain a call she can't ignore. She has her baton in her left hand and the shield in the other, and is forced to pull the shield to her chest to get along the hall-way. It's a circular shield, made of reinforced plastic.

She whacks the light switch at the bottom of the stairs and the stairwell lights up. Holding the shield above her head, she jerks her head at Mo, indicating for him to get his head under too. He's clutching the first-aid kit in one hand, his baton in the other. The stairs consist of about fifteen straight steps, which then curve round to the left. They can't see any further than the curve.

'We're going up, eyes and ears open, ready for anything.'

'Ready for anything.' He nods, his jaw tight.

'Police!' she shouts, in her loudest voice. 'We're coming up! Show yourselves!'

A sudden ruckus from above: the squeak of a door, running footsteps, a loud thud, then silence.

Penny starts walking up the stairs. She holds the shield above her head, her torso pressed to the wall, her neck craning to look above her. Mo's head is tucked close to hers, his breath hot on her neck, as they take the steps together. The Perspex shield is clear, allowing Penny to look upwards. She is just approaching the curve of the stairs when something explodes on top of the shield. The noise is enormous, and she lets out an unintelligible shout, instinctively ducking her head and twisting her face away from the impact. The sound is unmistakably the shattering of glass – she sees the image of a petrol bomb in her head – it takes her brain a beat to convince itself she's not on fire. Thousands of shards of glass fall across her shoulders and around their feet.

'More units required now at our location,' Mo is shouting into his radio. 'Suspect's throwing bottles.' Penny can hear the effort it is taking him to keep his voice steady. The radio starts to pipe up with units assigning themselves to their call for help, but she doesn't know where the units are and how long it will be until they get here, and she can't concentrate on that now because they're being attacked. 'We should go,' Mo shouts at her. 'Wait for back-up.'

She nods at him, *fuck this*, just as a desperate shout sounds from above them.

'Help!' It's a male voice, and he sounds young and desperate. 'He's going to kill us!'

She shakes her head and meets Mo's eye. With an almost imperceptible nod of his head, he agrees to press forward. Adrenaline pumps through her, and she forces her shaking legs to push forward up the stairs. They come around the curve cautiously, the crunching of glass grating against her nerves with every step, until Penny can see that the landing is empty. There's a cluster of empty alcohol bottles on the floor, just at the top of the stairs, and Penny imagines that these were the source of the glass lobbed at her and Mo seconds before. She lowers the shield and holds it at chest height in front of her, shaking herself, as small shards of glass crunch beneath her boots.

'Police!' she shouts again. 'We've got the place surrounded! Show yourself, come out with your hands up!'

Off the landing, which is around a metre square, are three doors. One on the left, one on the right and one directly opposite the stairs. Penny wishes she'd asked the drunk woman outside for more details about the layout of the flat. It has fallen silent once more. The doors to their left and right are open, the third is closed. To the left, Penny can see into a bedroom. On the right, a bathroom. She nods to Mo to watch the door on the left and points to the bathroom. Holding her baton above her head, *ready to strike*, her heart is thumping in her ears as she steps around the corner of the bathroom door. It's empty. There's blood in the sink and drops on the floor. She's aware that she doesn't want to disturb any potential crime scene, but life comes first. Their lives, and the life of the man who was shouting for help.

'Clear,' she says, in a low voice, turning to step back onto the landing. Mo takes the lead into the bedroom, whilst she stands behind him, keeping one eye on the third door. As she is turning her head back and forth, she notices a bloody handprint on the doorframe of the bedroom, right next to Mo's head.

'In here! Help us!'

The shouts come from behind the closed door.

'Empty,' Mo whispers to Penny.

'Control from 1972,' Penny talks low into the radio, 'where's the ambo?'

'Should be with you in a couple of minutes, 1972.'

'Any sign of that back-up?'

'Closest unit is five minutes out.'

'Suspect still on scene – not detained – tell ambo to wait outside until I tell you it's safe.'

'All received.'

Mo looks at her. 'Going in?'

'Back-up's nearly here,' she affirms, even though every ounce of sense she has is screaming at her to leave the flat. 'We need to help them.'

Mo nods, and approaches the door, grabbing the handle and looking back at her to make sure she is ready. Penny raises her baton and nods in reply.

*

The door swings open into a kitchen-diner. The space is open-plan, and immediately they can see that there's only two men in the room. They are cowering as far away from the door as possible, one on the floor holding his stomach, hands covered in blood, one squatting beside him. They look up in horror as the door swings open, before relief spreads across their faces as they see Penny and Mo.

'Did you get him?' the older of the men asks.

'Where is he?' Mo shouts, looking around the room in confusion.

Penny runs towards the men on the floor, quickly kneeling beside the younger of the two to assess his injuries. 'Where did he go?'

'He went the way you just came in.' The older man, panting heavily and drenched in sweat, points to the door where Mo is standing.

'He went out that way, Mo!'

Penny turns to look at Mo, a confused look on his face as he says, 'How did he get past us?' He lowers his baton as he widens his arms in a questioning manner.

In a flash, a figure appears behind him.

Penny tries to warn Mo, but it's too late, his name rips out of her mouth – *Mo!* – at exactly the same time that Nick Brooks brings an empty vodka bottle down over Mo's head. She watches in horror as Mo crumples to the floor.

She presses her fingers into her emergency button, located at the top of her personal radio and screams their location – '*Officer down! Urgent assistance needed now!*' Her emergency radio immediately begins to emit a bleeping alarm and vibrates against her shoulder. She doesn't care about the fear in her voice. She wants her colleagues to hear it. Wants them to come. Wants anyone who's not already on the way to run for their cars. *They're not going to be here in time.*

She stands, putting herself in front of the men on the floor. She takes her CS spray canister out of her kit belt and widens her stance, pointing the gas at Nick. Her other arm is raised, holding her baton. She wishes she had a taser, but she's not done the training course and there aren't enough to go around.

Nick is staring at her from the ingress, the broken bottle in his hand. She recognizes him as soon as she sees him. His eyes are wide and frantic.

'Stay where you are!' she shouts from the deepest part of her gut. *Make yourself big.* 'Don't come any closer.'

Her eyes flick to Mo, devastatingly still on the floor, blood seeping from a head wound.

'I'm not moving,' Nick says to her, raising the broken bottle and stabbing it in her direction. 'You have the devil behind you.'

She ignores him, fighting the urge to spin round. *He's rambling nonsense. How do you negotiate with crazy?*

'Nick,' she says, trying to talk in a low, calm voice, 'I need you to put the bottle down.'

'I'm not going back to hospital,' Nick says. He looks down towards Mo and shouts, 'I know who you really are.'

'Nick!' Penny shouts, trying desperately to get his attention away from Mo and onto her; she's only got to keep him talking for another couple of minutes. Back-up must be here soon. She considers spraying him, but fears that in this small, enclosed space, she will disable herself just as much as him. 'There's lots of police on the way here right now, you need to put down the bottle before they get here.'

Nick ignores her, bending closer to Mo. 'Let's cut off your piggy disguise.'

'Nick!' Penny shouts. 'Please put down the bottle!'

Nick raises the bottle so that the jagged ends are pointing at Mo. Penny's mind kicks into overdrive – *he's going to stab him* – and she sees Mo's Facebook profile in her head, his pretty wife and smiling baby, and suddenly she can hear sirens in the distance and she's running at Nick as fast as she can, jumping at him with all her strength, only one thought running through her mind again and again: *save Mo save Mo save Mo.*

She slams into Nick Brooks and they both hurtle onto the tiny landing. The sound of breaking glass detonates around her like a bomb. She feels a dull pain in her left shoulder as they fall onto the floor together, and she pushes herself away from him, trying to pull herself up and onto his chest, so that she can pin him to the ground. She pushes with both her arms but her left one is not working, and she slams into the floor as Nick twists out from below her. She feels the pressure of his weight as he flips her onto her back, crawling on top of her until his full weight is on her chest and she can't breathe.

She tries to shout, tries to hit him with her baton, but he's too close and she only has one arm. He's screaming at the top of his voice and Penny fights a wave of dizziness that threatens to make her close her eyes. The sirens are louder now. She just has to stay alive for another few minutes. She twists her one good arm between them and pushes with all her might as Nick screams whilst on top of her, raining blows down onto her face, neck and arms. Her eyes begin to sting and she can't move her arms any more. Her mind is screaming *fight* but her body won't respond. It's getting hard to breathe.

She can hear the sound of shouting, heavy boots on the stairs, and she knows that her friends have arrived.

You stopped him from stabbing Mo.

Penny stops fighting the exhaustion that's pulling her under and closes her eyes.

The young man at the scene had been stabbed in the stomach by Nick Brooks. Nick had used a knife that he had taken from the flat's kitchen. The man lost a lot of blood at the scene but recovered well with no lasting effects.

Police Constable Mohammed Amin needed five stitches in his scalp and received a severe concussion after Brooks hit him over the head with an empty vodka bottle. He spent a few hours in hospital and recovered quickly at home.

Police Constable Penny Curtis received severe lacerations to her left shoulder, caused by the broken bottle in Nick's hand. He also stabbed her three times, once in the cheek and twice more in her injured shoulder. He used the same knife that he had used to stab the young man. Penny was in hospital for over a week and needed two surgeries and plastic surgery on her left shoulder. She will never regain the full use of this limb.

In court, Nick Brooks admitted assaulting all involved, during a 'psychotic episode'. He was cleared of the attempted murder of PC Curtis and instead found guilty of causing grievous bodily harm with intent. He was jailed for fifteen years, to be served in a secure psychiatric hospital.

Police Constable Penelope Curtis served twenty-two years in the Yorkshire Police Service before being medically retired. She has since been diagnosed with PTSD, as a result of the savage attack on herself and her colleague. Police Constable Mohammed Amin credits her with saving his life, and both officers were nominated for the National Police Bravery Awards. She is proud of what she achieved in her long policing career, and during her service she received an award for Extraordinary Police Service, as well as two Chief Constable's Commendations.

When asked if she could go back and decide again whether to join the police service, she said, *'I'd do it all again in a heartbeat.'*

About the Author

Alice Vinten spent over ten years in the Metropolitan Police Service as a constable. Her memoir about life on the beat – *On the Line: Life – and Death – in the Metropolitan Police* (Two Roads) – received excellent reviews and led to her becoming a crime and police commentator for national media, as well as working with the BBC and other television production companies on various police dramas and documentaries. She lives with her children near the sea in Essex.

Acknowledgements

Firstly, I'd like to thank the inspiring policewomen who took part in the creation of this book. The decision was made early on to keep all contributors anonymous. This was to protect the officers, the people they have helped, the victims, as well as the families of those affected by the stories I've shared. Most of the women I interviewed for *The Real Happy Valley* have spent thirty years or more in the police service, and their knowledge, professionalism and dedication to protecting the public shone through in every interview I conducted. These women are brave, intelligent, formidable and, most importantly, kind.

To the women who shared their stories – you know who you are – THANK YOU. I feel extremely privileged to have been able to share your experiences with the public.

To female police officers everywhere – thank you for your service. Thank you for daring to take on a 'man's world', for standing strong in the face of the misogyny that many of us have faced, and for proving that women can do absolutely anything a man can. I have the greatest of respect for you.

To Sally Wainwright, for being one of the only screen-writers out there to champion the stories of middle-aged women, for succeeding in putting the lives of middle-aged women back in the spotlight, for proving that we still have something to say, and that we're worth listening to. In creating Catherine Cawood, you've given a voice to police-women across Yorkshire and beyond. To Lisa Farrand (some would call you the *real* Catherine), thank you for your time, and for connecting me with some of the wonderful police-women of Yorkshire.

To my agent, the indomitable Eve White, thank you for continually believing in me, and fighting my corner. To all of the wonderful team at Transworld Books – Zoe, Steph, Lucy, Chloë, Tom, Melissa, Judith, Phil and Holly (apologies if I've forgotten anyone!) – thank you for all your hard work, encouragement and support. Thank you Tony for designing the incredible cover – I love it!

Lastly, as always, huge love and respect to my mother and father for their constant support and encouragement, and to my funny, clever and kind boys – you inspire me every day.